Aspects of Learning and Memory

Aspects
of Learning and Memory

Edited by **Derek Richter**

William Heinemann Medical Books Limited
London

First published 1966

Printed in Great Britain by The Whitefriars Press Ltd
London and Tonbridge

Contents

Contributors

J. B. BRIERLEY, M.D., F.C.Path.
Medical Research Council Neuropsychiatric Research Unit, Carshalton, Surrey.

SIR JOHN GADDUM, Sc.D., F.R.S.
Institute of Animal Physiology, Babraham, Cambridge.

B. MELDRUM, M.B., Ph.D.
Medical Research Council Neuropsychiatric Research Unit, Carshalton, Surrey.

MARYSE METCALFE, Dip. Psych. App.
Medical Research Council Neuropsychiatric Research Unit, Carshalton, Surrey.

DEREK RICHTER, Ph.D., M.R.C.P.
Medical Research Council Neuropsychiatric Research Unit, Carshalton, Surrey.

IAN STEELE RUSSELL, Ph.D.
Medical Research Council Unit for the Experimental Investigation of Behaviour, University College, London.

PROF. W. RITCHIE RUSSELL, M.D., F.R.C.P.
Department of Neurology, The Radcliffe Infirmary, Oxford.

Preface

This book was written by a group of scientists working in different fields of research, but sharing a common interest in the problem of memory. Each chapter gives a different viewpoint. The first three, written by a psychologist, a clinical neurologist and a pathologist, deal with various aspects of memory in man; the remaining four chapters relate to basic aspects and pursue the problem further into the fields of physiology, biochemistry and animal behaviour.

Drafts of the chapters were discussed at informal meetings at Carshalton, held generally at the "Fox and Hounds". The final versions were written independently and they therefore contain certain points of agreement and disagreement. Both are informative. Steps were taken to avoid any extensive duplication, but since it was planned that each chapter should be complete in itself, some experimental work is discussed in more than one place. It appeared that some overlapping of this kind might not be a bad thing if it helped to link up the viewpoints of workers in different fields of research. This purpose is served also by including a general chapter on the "neurological basis of learning" which brings together psychological as well as physiological data on mechanisms operating in animals and in man. This chapter is modified from an essay published separately in *Perspectives in Biology and Medicine*, and we are indebted to the editor, Dr Dwight J. Ingle, for permission to reproduce material from the original article.

Sir John Gaddum died on June 30th, 1965. The chapter appearing in this book is the last of his scientific publications. Those who knew him will feel no surprise at his courage in completing a task of this kind during a time of physical as well as mental stress. We are indebted to Lady Gaddum for making the final corrections to his chapter.

During the discussion of the different chapters it became evident that the same word is sometimes used in different fields of research to mean quite different things. This may lead to confusion if the different meanings are not recognized, or to advances in knowledge if they are. The following statements about the usage of the words "learning" and "memory" are intended, not as rigid definitions, but rather as illustrations of the large number of different ways in which these words are used.

It is a pleasure to acknowledge our indebtedness to Francis Schmitt, who has kindly made available to us the very stimulating bulletins of the Neurosciences Research Program. Current interest in learning and memory is such that there is now an extensive literature on the subject.

We would like to emphasize that this book deals only with certain limited aspects of the problem and there are undoubtedly important lines of research which it has not been possible to include.

Carshalton, Surrey   DEREK RICHTER
January, 1966

Meaning of the Words 'Learning' and 'Memory'

LEARNING

Common language In the common language (1) learning is the act or *process* of acquiring knowledge or skill by study, practice or experience. Such learning requires memory, but does not necessarily involve *remembering*, which is the recall of past experience to conscious recognition. In a different sense of the word, (2) learning is knowledge acquired by study.

Biology (3) Learning is a general term for the reorganization of behaviour as a result of individual experience. Learning thus serves to modify patterns of behaviour which are inborn or instinctive, and therefore not attributable to learning.

Psychology Different kinds of learning have been classified and named in various different ways. The following classes of learning processes have been commonly recognized: they are not mutually exclusive.

(4) *Associative learning* is a general term for forms of learning in which one stimulus, word or idea becomes associated with another by being paired regularly with it. One stimulus can thereby acquire some of the properties of the other stimulus. Associative learning is involved in the classical conditioning experiments of Pavlov (Type I or respondent conditioning) in which a response normally resulting from one stimulus (US) comes to be elicited by another stimulus (CS) through repeated presentation of both stimuli together or of the conditioned stimulus (CS) a short time before the unconditioned stimulus (US).

(5) *Instrumental learning* (contingency learning) means learning what to do in any situation in which a goal can be attained only by making an appropriate response. An example of this (known as "operant conditioning") is when a hungry rat learns to press a lever to get a pellet of food. Another example (known as "Type II conditioning" or "avoidance conditioning") is when an animal learns to avoid an unpleasant stimulus such as an electric shock by making a particular response. In these situations the correct response can be regarded as a contingency which is instrumental in attaining an objective.

(6) *Learning set.* When an animal performs a series of learning tests it may learn to adopt a general approach described as "learning set", which enables it to learn a new task more rapidly by taking short-cuts. The adoption of a learning set can be regarded as "learning to learn".

(7) *Perceptual learning* is a general name for learning of the kind in which an animal gains information about the environment without necessarily making any overt response. The animal's perception of the environment is thereby changed. This occurs in "sensory–sensory learning" in which an animal learns to associate one stimulus with

another: it occurs also in "insight" which is a discontinuous process in which something in an immediate situation is combined with something remote.

(8) *Habituation* is the process of gradually becoming adapted to a continuing stimulus or situation; it is shown by the gradual waning of a response. Habituation is one form of a more general kind of learning ("redundancy learning") in which an animal learns to reject or to disregard a stimulus or situation that is irrelevant to its needs.

(9) *Discriminitive learning* is any form of learning which requires an animal to discriminate between two different stimuli. It may mean learning to attend to the particular cues in a stimulus situation needed to evoke one response rather than another.

(10) *Latent learning* is learning which may occur during an intervening period of activity which does not involve the task that is being learned. It is shown by an improved performance after the intervening period. Latent learning may be a consequence of "incidental learning", in which the motive is not evident.

(11) *Concept learning* (logical learning; meaningful learning; sub-stance learning) is learning in which the meaning is abstracted from the material presented. It is shown by recognition of the meaning of what was studied, without regard for the original form.

(12) *Rote learning* (learning by heart; verbatim learning; mechanical learning) means learning material so that it can be reproduced in the exact form in which it was presented, without trying to understand it.

(13) *Imprinting* is a form of rapid learning which occurs at a particular time in very early life, as when a young bird forms an attachment to the mother bird. It is characteristically hard to extinguish.

(14) *Conditioning* is the process occurring in an animal (or the pro-cedure used) in establishing a conditioned response. The word condition-ing is also commonly used in a wider sense for learning of any kind. The term "conditioned stimulus" came into use originally through the mistranslation of an expression used by Pavlov meaning "condition*al* stimulus": it implies that the elicitation of a particular response is conditional on the establishment of an association with another stimulus. To condition an animal means to establish a conditioned response, or simply to make it learn.

(15) *"Pseudoconditioning"* ("pseudo-learning") is a term that has been used to describe a behavioural change wrongly attributed to learning and really due to other factors such as fatigue, changed sensitivity or a change in the environmental conditions.

MEMORY

Common language   In the common language, the word memory is used loosely for: (1) the *faculty* by which facts or past experiences are called to mind; "notes help the memory"; (2) the *capacity* for remembrance, e.g. for remembering to carry out duties or other observances at the appropriate time; (3) an individual item, or the total store, of that which is remembered; "happy childhood memories"; (4) a *period* during which events are remembered; "within living memory"; and (5) an *act* of commemoration, "in loving memory of". In the common language the word is used only in relation to conscious beings; but the concept of memory is sometimes extended to include the capacity to retain learned skills, as for example reading and writing, or driving a car.

Biology Memory is regarded as a property of certain living organisms which helps them to adapt to the conditions of their environment. Memory may be defined as (6) the capacity of an organism to behave in a way which is modified by previous experience. In this sense of the word, memory, which includes motor skills and is not necessarily at a conscious level, includes the capacity for *conditioning* and for *delayed response*, i.e. responding to an external stimulus when there is a delay between the reception of a stimulus and the permitted response to it.

In the term *genetic memory* the word is used in a figurative sense to describe (7) the total store of information contained in the genetic apparatus (chromosomes, etc.) of the living cell. Such information is not acquired by learning: during embryonic and later development it enables the organism to develop the characteristics of its predecessors, and so to recapitulate the phylogenetic history of the species.

The term *collective memory* has been used for (8) specific patterns of behaviour (mating, nest-building, migration) inherited by all members of a species or of a genetic strain.

The term *plasticity* is used by physiologists for the property of undergoing a permanent functional change in response to a physiological stimulus. Memory is not a physiological term.

Information theory The term memory is used in a figurative sense for (9) the information storage systems incorporated in computers and other machines to control their operation.

Neurology Brain injuries can lead to the selective loss of certain kinds of memory while other kinds remain relatively unimpaired. On this basis it is possible to distinguish roughly between certain specific types of memory which differ in the retention span: (10) *immediate memory*, is temporary and lasts for no more than a few minutes; this is long enough, for example, to hold a conversation or to perform a simple mental calculation; (11) *recent memory* refers to events during a period extending from about 10 minutes to a few months back, and (12) *long-term memory* includes memories of a more permanent kind extending back to childhood. The term (13) *short-term memory*, which is also used, is ambiguous, since it may refer to immediate memory or recent memory or both. In any case it is usually better to state the retention span.

Loss of memory for events in the period immediately preceding a brain injury is known as *retrograde amnesia;* this may be due in part to impairment of recall, since a part of the memory tends to return in time. Loss of memory for events immediately following a brain injury is known as anterograde or *post-traumatic amnesia.* A sense of familiarity, wrongly attributed to memory, is described as the *déjà vu* phenomenon.

Psychology Memory has been regarded classically as involving several distinct mechanisms; (a) impression, (b) retention, (c) re-emergence or recall, and (d) recognition. Learning requires attention, perception and selection of the matter that is retained. Selection is influenced by motivational (affective) factors, and retention by the process of reviewing learned material and consolidating by rehearsal. It has sometimes been assumed that retention requires a physical alteration in the nervous tissue of the brain; this has been called the "organic memory", "memory trace" or "engram". Recall may be effected by the activation of a memory trace; it is influenced by suggestion and by emotional (affective) factors.

As in the common language, the word memory is used in several different senses. It is used as (14) a general term for the function of reviving (reliving) past experiences, for (15) the total store of things that can be remembered and for (16) any one particular experience that is called to mind. Several special kinds of memory have been described: (17) *Rote memory* is the capacity for reproducing material (which may be meaningless) in the exact form in which it was presented. (18) *Logical memory* is the capacity for reproducing the essential substance or meaning of learned material without the original form. (19) *Visual memory* is a type of memory in which visual imagery is mainly concerned. (20) *Auditory memory* is the memory for sound. The term memory is normally used in psychology for material consciously learned, but the term (21) *unconscious memory* has been used for functions conditioned at an unconscious level and later recalled to consciousness. The same term (22) *unconscious memory* is also used in psychoanalysis for emotionally charged material (affects) and ideas which have been repressed, but which may reach consciousness in disguised forms. Psychologists have described as (23) *short-term memory* the retention of sensory impressions which may persist for no more than a fraction of a second.

D.R.

Problems of Memory in Man

Maryse Metcalfe

I. Remembering and Forgetting

We generally take for granted our ability to remember the past, and we tend to speak of this ability in terms of its short-comings, in terms of what we forget. If I say of myself that I have a poor memory, I may mean that I easily forget to telephone the grocer or to answer a personal letter, that faces, pictures, places fade out of my mind or that I seldom recognize places which I know I have visited previously. I envy those who can not only visualize places with ease but also can find their way through the streets of a town visited years ago. I can, however, recognize at once, in the first few pages, a novel I have read long ago even if the title or the author's name eludes me.

Some people find it comparatively easy to recall deliberately a sentence from a conversation, a name or a telephone number. Few are able to recreate a taste or a smell at will; yet a particular scent—perhaps the sweet smell of freshly sawn wood after rain—may bring a rush of vivid childhood memories to the mind.

These examples show that memory takes many different forms. Memory may be associated with sound or taste or only with abstract thought. Its content can be pleasant or unpleasant. The recollection of an event may be intentional and indeed may require painful mental effort. On the other hand, it may be triggered off quite accidentally by some outside occurrence apparently unrelated to it; the link between the present and the past event may be tenuous in the extreme.

Memory is an ambiguous term. It always implies some relationship in time, some connexion between a present impression and a past event. Very probably this distinction between past and present is consciously recognized only by man.

The mechanism by which we recall the past is frequently a process of matching a present image with a past image. This matching can be a conscious examination of several possibilities. I see, for example, a face at a party and spend the whole evening searching my mind for a remembrance of that face which would give me a clue as to its identity. Suddenly, I know for certain that the face I have just seen matches one I know: that of the dentist or of the swimming-instructor whom I had only seen in a very different context. Similarly, I may attempt to repeat a poem which I have learnt a while ago. I can achieve this by successive approximations of the lines until I finally reach the point where the poem, as I repeat it now, appears to me exactly identical with the one I had learnt. The successful matching of a present image with a past image involves a process of recognition. This is at least partly what we mean by "recall".

Another mechanism of human memory is the process of assimilation of a new impression, which consists of the translation of that impression into words or other symbols. It is this verbal assimilation which makes possible the communication of remembered material to others in the form of knowledge, tradition or history.

These two mechanisms help us in attempting to define human memory. In its wide, biological sense, memory is a process whereby past experience leaves a trace which may be revealed as a modification in the behaviour of the living organism. In human memory, however, past experience may also be relived by being recalled to present consciousness.

The term memory, even when it is used in this narrow sense, is an abstraction: it covers a complex group of mental activities, some of which can be observed, others only inferred. One day, I read the account of a political incident in the newspaper; I must somehow have retained it, for the next day or years later I will recall it; or I may then try to recall it and fail; I have forgotten all of it or some of the details. Thus, memory includes at least three stages: acquisition or registration; storing or retention; and recall or recognition.

Most of our knowledge about memory comes from studying, by introspective examination or by experiments, the extent, content and qualities of remembered material. We still know very little about acquisition and we know almost nothing about the active mental processes which must occur between the moment an impression is recorded and the moment when it is wholly or partly remembered.

Memory implies that, in some manner, impressions can be stored. As the storing of individual replicas of the original impressions would be a physical impossibility, storing must involve the transformation, coding and assimilation of those impressions. Although we know little about the "positive" processes involved in remembering, we know slightly more about their negative counterpart—that is, forgetting.

Of the multitude of impressions that continuously assail our senses, the vast majority are almost certainly not recorded and they can therefore never be available for recall. It is inappropriate to speak of forgetting in relation to those unrecorded impressions. Other impressions, which we have voluntarily or involuntarily at some time committed to memory, may become temporarily or permanently unavailable for recall. This is what we mean when we speak of forgetting.

It is easier to examine what causes this forgetting than to understand how remembering takes place, and this chapter will deal mainly with the factors that influence forgetting. They can be classified as follows:

1. Delay between the receiving of an original impression and the recalling of it.
2. Intervention of other mental activities.
3. Receptiveness of the person who remembers.
   This can be affected by:
   (a) Innate or acquired qualities of the person.
   (b) Temporary or permanent pathological conditions.
4. Environment.
5. Organization and transformation of the material.

Methods of assessment of memory It may be useful here to indicate some of the ways in which memory (or forgetting) is assessed for clinical or experimental purposes. Of the three stages of memory, only the third one (recall or recognition) is amenable to direct observation and measurement. This measurement is usually limited to short-term memory (about a few minutes). It is far more difficult to assess long-term memory, such as the recall of personal experiences, with any real precision.

Short-term memory can be assessed by the ability to repeat, after a short interval of time, material that has been presented once only, and also by learning tests in which material is presented many times. In the first case, varied material can be used: the subject is asked to reproduce exactly a list of figures, a sentence or a paragraph with as many details as possible. To test visual memory, designs are presented or flashed on a screen. Auditory memory can be tested in children by getting them to tap a rhythm of sounds. In all these tests, however, intelligence and age play a part in determining the results. Although some of these tests have been grouped and the mean of their scores is deemed to represent a "memory quotient", it is in fact very difficult to assess a factor of memory independent of age and intellectual level.

A type of material which has been extensively used since it was introduced by Ebbinghaus over eighty years ago, is "nonsense syllables". Lists of three-letter syllables (TAS, ZIN, VEC) have been prepared with care to ensure that they have as little associative meaning as possible. Such syllables are usually spelt out or presented one at a time on a "memory-drum".

Learning tests allow for several trials until the subject can reproduce the learnt material to a given criterion. Material is again quite varied. A sentence or the definitions of some new words can be learnt. A method frequently used is that of paired associates. Unrelated words are learnt in pairs; at recall time only one word from each pair is called and the subject has to recall the second word. A test of paired associates can include visual symbols or new words said to belong to some unknown language.

One can also measure the saving in learning time which occurs when a subject has to re-learn to perfection material which he had already learnt a while ago.

Long-term memory is assessed by the recall of personal experiences or of social events such as the name of the winner of a race or that of the Prime Minister. It is not easy to carry out this assessment with any real precision; comparison between subjects is difficult partly because events may vary in their importance and partly because events of long ago may have been more or less often rehearsed.

Although most of these tests are rough they can be helpful in detecting abnormal memory impairment due to various causes such as brain damage.

II. Delay Between Impression and Recall

How quickly do we forget? It is common experience that a long delay in time between what we see or hear and the moment when we wish to recall it, leads to forgetting. The rapid forgetting following a single impression has been taken as evidence for "trace decay"; that is that a memory trace tends to undergo deterioration with the passage of time. It is difficult to show experimentally that a supposed trace will in fact disappear with time alone. One would need an interval of time empty of all mental activity; this is made only partly possible when the impression and the recall are separated by a period of sleep or by a period of drug-induced unconsciousness.

It is intriguing to know whether sleep favours remembering. Experiments have been carried out in which two students learned a list of syllables; one student learned it before a period of normal activity and the second student just before he went to sleep. The experiment was repeated for similar periods of sleep or of activity of 1, 2, 4 and 8 hours. After each period of sleep the number of syllables recalled was greater than after a similar period of activity, although some forgetting did occur even after a period of sleep (Jenkins and Dallenbach, 1924). This experiment does not fulfil exactly the condition of an empty interval, for sleep does include some degree of nervous activity. Moreover, the student who went to sleep was bound to have had a short period between the learning and the sleep, when he was still awake and able to rehearse what he had learnt.

This leads to the consideration of what mental activities cause forgetting.

III. Interference and Facilitation

Any new impression and its recall are separated by an interval during which numerous activities may take place. Laboratory experiments are but a simplified and schematic representation of the usual sequence of events: they may introduce another learning task between the first learning and the recall. The main results of such experiments show that:

1. A learning task intervening between the original learning of some

material and the recall of that material causes a decrease in the amount of material recalled.

2. The closer the similarity between the original material and the intervening activity (for instance, when both concern the learning of nonsense syllables) the greater the forgetting of the original material.
3. The longer the rest period between the original learning and the intervening activity the higher the amount of recall.
4. Material learnt *before* the original learning task also has a detrimental effect on the amount recalled.

Forgetting is thus affected by the nature and the timing of the events which fill a time interval. Retroactive interference is defined as the decrease in remembering which is brought about by the intervention of some particular mental activity between the original learning and the recall. Proactive interference is that caused by associations or learnt material stored before the particular event that we are trying to recall.

An investigation reported by Underwood (1964) shows the striking effect of proactive interference. This investigation was intended to ascertain the effects of delay in time on the ability to recall. Tests were carried out in each of which a student was presented with nonsense syllables, one at a time, and then asked to recall one of them after a short interval of time up to 18 seconds. An analysis of the results indicated that the students tended to retain the syllables much longer at the beginning of each test than at the end. For example, responses made after 18 seconds were almost always correct when given at the beginning of the test, whereas at the end, responses made after 18 seconds were almost always incorrect: the efforts made by the students in the earlier part of the tests seemed to interfere with their success later on. Thus the investigation strongly suggests that proactive interference is a much more important cause of forgetting than delay in time. Indeed interference is considered by many theorists to be the main factor responsible for forgetting.

Why interference has a detrimental effect is not clear. It may be that during the process of acquiring some new knowledge, items of previous knowledge have to be suppressed. Other possible explanations could apply both to retroactive and to proactive interference. For example, the mechanism of recall may be such that it ceases to operate when faced with competing solutions to a task of recall—solutions which are either very similar or very numerous.

Some period of *consolidation* seems to be necessary after learning, for material to become resistant to interference, and the longer that period the greater the resistance. This consolidation may be partly an assimilation (or re-coding) of the material into the individual's web of past learning. As yet consolidation has been very little studied experimentally. One experimenter (Zinkin, 1965) investigated the disruption of the human memory trace by presenting two types of material (familiar and unfamiliar) to psychiatric patients just before they were given electro-convulsive therapy (E.C.T.). She measured the accuracy of their reten-tion by testing them five hours after E.C.T. Her results suggest that the traces for the familiar type of material consolidated rapidly and were unaffected by the E.C.T. applied one minute later. In contrast the un-familiar material took longer to consolidate and was still vulnerable to disruption after the one minute interval.

The numerous learning activities we engage in interfere with those that precede or follow them, but the importance of interference may well have been exaggerated because of the many ingenious psychological experiments which have brought it into evidence.

If previous or intervening learning always had a detrimental effect on recall or on new learning, bright and alert children who seek and acquire plenty of new bits of information would recall less than the slow, dull child. It would also follow that the more education we get the less we can recall. As this is not so, some process of facilitation as well as inter-ference must take place. The old idea that learning Latin teaches us the rules of logic may be discredited, but learning a skill or a language often helps with the learning of another. We learn to learn and our whole idea of education is based on the assumption that the extent of our know-ledge will make new learning easier.

IV. Receptiveness

In most laboratory experiments, the subjects are assumed to be alert, keen and co-operative, and to concentrate single-mindedly on the tests at hand. Incidental interference is avoided. Fatigue and hunger can be controlled. In real life all these influences are bound to come into action. The material which we shall later retain may have a more or less in-formative meaning. It may be accompanied by an emotional association. Other tasks may be competing with it. Attention may be directed elsewhere.

Among the conditions necessary for the reception or assimilation of an impression, the degree of alertness and attention (arousal) is import-ant. Verbal memory tests have been used in conjunction with physio-logical measurements of the level of arousal (for instance, changes in skin resistance or changes in electrical activities in the brain). A very high level of arousal at the time of learning of new material was apparently linked with poor recall after a few minutes. Yet those items where learning had been associated with a high level of arousal were the best remembered ones after a period of 45 minutes or of one week (Walker, 1962).

Generally speaking, an individual's receptiveness and his ability to receive, filter and integrate impressions have an important effect on the proportion of material that is subsequently forgotten. One can go further and consider whether intelligence and certain personality characteristics and attitudes influence remembering and forgetting.

The capacity to acquire, retain and recall information is only partly related to the level of an individual's intelligence. Mental defectives do show poor memory but this appears to be due more to a defect in acquisition than to an inability to retain or to recall. Acquisition of new material is difficult for them for many reasons, which include a low state of arousal, lack of interest, and lack of understanding. However, imbeciles, who have learnt some easy material to the same degree as normal children (having, of course, taken longer to do so) are able to reproduce that material as well as the normal children after the span of retention for which they were all tested (O'Connor and Hermelin, 1963). When one tries to assess whether more intelligent people remember better, the difficulty lies in devising the sort of tests which will measure a capacity for remembering and not merely the capacity for making logical or imaginative associations which will bring the learnt material back to mind.

There appears to be a limited relationship between memory capacity and the level of intelligence, but this has not yet been generalized to all types of memory and all levels of intelligence (Ingham, 1952). It is all the more striking, in view of this assumed relationship, to observe loss of memory in organically impaired or elderly people whose general intelligence shows little deterioration.

Some types of conditioning have been related to types of personality, but the more complex processes of memory and forgetting have not been much studied in this way, except for a phenomenon with which we are all familiar: the improvement in recall which occurs after a period of rest. This improvement has been shown to vary greatly according to the type of activity and also to the drive of the subject, to his state of fatigue (lack of sleep, drugs, overwork) and finally to his personality type (Eysenck, 1964).

The effect of emotion associated with a definite impression, on the later recall of that impression, is difficult to evaluate. Experiments relating to an emotional incident accompanying the impression are of necessity crude. Subjects are asked to memorize lists of syllables; certain lists are presented together with an unexpected event which is meant to shock the subject (his chair collapses, part of the ceiling falls on him, etc.); the recall of the lists associated with shock is demonstrably poorer than the recall of the other lists (Harden, 1930). This sequence of events, which can be said to interfere with the necessary consolidation period, is very different from the subtle emotional contexts, pleasant or unpleasant, experienced in life. It is also important to distinguish between the emotional context of an impression and its emotional content. The latter may lead either to enhancement or to repression of the memory.

Experimental results usually indicate that pleasant impressions are better retained than the unpleasant ones.

Repression is the symptom of avoiding certain thoughts for fear of the association they may bring. In its most severe form, it leads to a blocking of thought and to an amnesia for a past period in life. Examples of repression abound in psychiatric literature. Some of the best documented cases are those of amnesia in soldiers in the World War II suffering from what was called "combat neuroses". These patients and similar ones are unable to recall some painful event and cannot follow any trend of thought which might lead to that event. Repression occurs in a milder form in everyday life. Most of our knowledge of repression is anecdotal and concerns the bill one forgets to pay or the meeting one forgets to attend for reasons which can become clear after some self-analysis. Such common repression of particular tasks, names or places has been abundantly illustrated in Freud's *Psycho-pathology of Everyday Life* (1914). It is understandably very difficult to study repression in an experimentally controlled situation.

V. Environment

Forgetting has also been defined as "inaccessibility of the memory trace" (Brown, 1964). It is a common occurrence that a forgotten item suddenly jumps to one's mind because of some chance association. A usual and helpful trick for remembering something forgotten is to put oneself back, mentally or actually, to the place where it was first thought about: the item which had momentarily disappeared from mind then comes back easily. Recall depends partly on the extent to which the environment prevailing during the acquisition also prevails when recall is demanded. It has been demonstrated experimentally that the re-learning of lists of syllables is much quicker when it takes place in exactly the same surroundings as the original learning (Greenspan and Raynaud, 1957).

More difficult to demonstrate experimentally, yet a common introspective observation, is the building of a mental frame in order to retrieve a forgotten item. If I try to remember when a certain event took place, I weave around it in my mind a web of temporal and factual details: what the weather was like, what I or other people wore at the time, and therefore what was the probable season of the year. I place it before or after some other incident. By weaving the web closer and closer I am able to narrow the possible dates to one only. Little work has been carried out on this mechanism, yet not only is it very frequent but it implies that memory is helped by man's capacity for organizing his past in relation to time; to keep, so to speak, a log-book.

VI. Reconstruction and Organization

Recall does not bring to mind a complete or incomplete "mirror" reproduction of a past impression. Much recall seems to be a reconstructive process based on partial retention and on the knowledge of what is probable. The impression itself is already a reconstruction. If I see from my window something red moving between the trees I should assume that this is the top of a London bus because I "know" it cannot be anything else. I shall retain the impression as such. When I recall the impression I shall have forgotten the coloured advertisements or the moving patches of shade on the bus. I may well not have noticed them at all originally. As I acquire the impression I shape it according to a definite framework in my mind. I shall in fact recall the whole bus and see it as No. 31 bus. If I find myself involved as a witness having to give evidence because that particular bus ran over a child, I may remember that it was going quite slowly at the time. The judge, however, before he accepts my evidence, will compare it with that of others who have witnessed the scene from a different angle or who, in the case of the child's parents or of the driver, played an active part in the accident.

Such modification and reconstruction of material occur clearly when we hear a story and pass it on. Professor Bartlett in Cambridge studied this procedure intensively (Bartlett, 1932). His methods of investigation closely followed life happenings and thus retained some of the richness and variety of mental experience. His studies have become a classic in the field of psychological investigation.

One of his experiments was in fact a controlled demonstration of the way in which rumour, traditions, etc. develop. He told a bizarre North American folk-tale to one single student who was asked to repeat it, as he recalled it, to a second student who then reported it to a third one and so on. This experiment was carried out again with several groups of students (and has since been reproduced by other investigators). The successive versions showed that progressive changes take place: the story, when re-told, was simpler, more organized and more coherent; irrelevant details or details which seemed incongruous to an English student were dropped. Similar observations were made when a student was asked to repeat the story after increasing intervals of time.

If such organization and reconstruction occur spontaneously and without guidance, what is the effect of teaching rules and methods of organizing information before committing it to memory? Professor Postman (1954) attempted to answer this question. He trained several groups of students to categorize items of information according to different rules. In a subsequent memory task, both the number of items recalled and the quality of the errors were influenced in each group of students by the rules for that group. Those students trained to categorize information in general retained it longer than an untrained group. They were also far less affected by retroactive interference. Postman used the results from this and similar experiments to emphasize that reorganization is the essential part of recall and that one's habits of mind are all important.

VII. Conclusion

It is astonishing that despite the many obstacles to remembering, so much of the past can still be voluntarily or involuntarily recalled. This may be due in part to certain special characteristics of memory in man. Memory enters into every kind of mental activity and the use of symbols to assimilate and classify impressions greatly extends the scope of human memory. Symbols such as those of music and mathematics, and especially those of verbal language, allow information retained in the human mind to be coordinated, structured, revised and finally communicated to others. By the use of symbols, a past impression can be recalled to present consciousness and a course of action critically reviewed. The ability to utilize conscious memory in this way is important, not only in the development of the individual but also in the cultural evolution of mankind.

References

Bartlett, F. C. (1932), *Remembering*, Macmillan, London.
Brown, J. (1964), *Brit. med. Bull.*, **20**, 8.
Eysenck, H. J. (1964), *Life Sci.*, **3**, 175.
Freud, S. (1914), *Psychopathology of Everyday Life*, Unwin, London.
Greenspan, I. and Raynaud, R. (1957), *J. exp. Psychol.*, **53**, 1.
Harden, L. M. (1930), *J. gen. Psychol.*, **3**, 197.
Ingham, J. (1952), *Brit. J. Psychol.*, **43**, 20.
Jenkins, J. G. and Dallenbach, K. M. (1924), *Amer. J. Psychol.*, **35**, 612.
O'Connor, N. and Hermelin, B. (1963), *Speech and Thought in Severe Subnormality*, Pergamon Press, Oxford.
Postman, L. (1954). *Psychol. Monogr.*, **68**, No. 3.
Underwood, B. J. (1964), *Sci. Amer.*, **210**, No. 3, 91.
Walker, E. I., Paper read at an AAAS meeting 1952, Quoted in Berlyne, D. (1964), *Ann. Rev. Psychol.*, **15**, 115.
Zinkin, S., Paper read at the B.P.S. Annual Conference 1965.

Contribution from Clinical Neurology

W. Ritchie Russell and Freda Newcombe

I. Introduction

Although little is known about the physiological mechanisms associated with learning and memory, it may be assumed that they involve the establishment of neuronal patterns which can be reactivated at a later date when remembrance occurs. These patterns may be maintained in complex reverberatory circuits whose repeated excitation leads to permanent structural changes (Hebb, 1949).

In clinical neurology, one may notice the break-up and disappearance of long established reactions and patterns in cases of brain disease: on the other hand, a failure in the capacity to add to existing patterns may develop—there is a loss of the ability to learn and to memorize. These two aspects of memory have to be clearly separated from each other, for the loss of the ability to learn is often observed without the disappearance of long established memories.

Only a minute fraction of the visual, auditory and other sensory bombardments of the normal brain are held for future use, and in the absence of some alerting process the afferent impulse patterns for the most part decay in a few seconds and are lost for ever. Evidence is accumulating that the memory trace swiftly decays in the absence of rehearsal (Conrad and Hille, 1958).

The processes of memorizing, of short-term memory or of learning, only operate if the brain is in a healthy state, and these cease completely during severe brain illnesses, during anæsthesia or during recovery from concussion. The failure to memorize after concussive head injuries leads to a period of amnesia for events after the injury and, in retrospect, is studied as the phenomenon of post-traumatic amnesia (P.T.A.). For this reason the duration of P.T.A. provides a most important indication in retrospect of the severity of the brain injury: the duration of disordered function bears a close relationship to the severity of injury to any part of the nervous system whether brain, spinal cord or nerve (Russell, 1964).

In cases of brain commotion from acceleration concussion, the recovery of orientation, and awareness of the environment and of the passage of time coincide with the return of the capacity to memorize, thus ending the period of P.T.A. During the period of traumatic confusion the patient's only memories are related to happenings before the accident, and not to current events. This leads to confusion, disorientation and confabulation during certain stages of recovery, yet the patient's behaviour may appear normal to the casual observer.

In some diseases this inability to form new memories occurs as a result of a localized disturbance to deeply situated parts of the brain concerned with the limbic system. This system seems to be specially concerned with the physiological mechanisms involved in adding new memories, and thus with maintaining awareness of the ever-changing environment of living (see below). Brain diseases affecting the limbic system directly may lead to this amnesic syndrome developing during the active stages of the illness, as for example in tuberculous meningitis (Williams and Smith, 1954) or in tumours in the third ventricle of the brain (Williams and Pennybacker, 1954).

The brain diseases which affect the alcoholic are chiefly caused by nutritional deficiencies and they may cause amnesic syndromes of this temporary nature, but if these encephalopathies are allowed to continue uncorrected a permanent alcoholic dementia ensues in which loss of memorizing is a prominent feature. This is the classical Korsakoff's psychosis, and the degenerative changes affecting the limbic system involve the mamillary bodies particularly. This syndrome is also recognized by the pathologists as Wernicke's encephalopathy (see Barbizet, 1963).

Certain forms of encephalitis affect particularly the hippocampal part of the limbic system and this may also lead to a permanent amnesic syndrome (Rose and Symonds, 1960). Surgical excision of the temporal lobe also removes the hippocampus but this must be destroyed or removed on both sides of the brain to produce the amnesic state. Such patients have gross difficulty in learning new material but show no loss of old professional skills nor difficulty in verbatim repetition (Scoville and Milner, 1957). Thus this isolated loss of ability to learn does not occur when structures on one side of the brain only are destroyed. Among the Oxford records of 1000 cases of brain wound incurred in World War II, there are some in which a small metal fragment had cut through the brain to the region of the third ventricle causing very little damage to the cerebral hemispheres and yet producing a specific and severe impairment of the capacity to memorize or to learn. It was characteristic of these wounds that the track of the missile crossed the midline not far from the third ventricle, and thus injured the limbic system of both the right and the left sides of the brain.

II. The Physiology of Learning

These clinical examples of bilateral disease or injury to the limbic system do not of course indicate that memory traces are stored in this system but that its activity plays an essential role in the establishment of memories elsewhere in the brain. It might be argued that this defect is one of recall and that the memory trace has been established, but this view is not really acceptable as far as learning new material is concerned.

Since the work of Moruzzi and Magoun (1949) on the brain stem arousal system and the animal experiments of Glickman (1961) and Mahut (1957) who produced defects of memory and of insightful learning in various conditions of sub-cortical stimulation, modern concepts of brain physiology have been very much concerned with the interaction of one brain system on another so as to influence thresholds of activity. In this way the hippocampal–fornix system must be concerned with driving other parts of the brain to develop memory traces.

This of course is only a small part of a complicated story. Thus every memory may have an associated emotional accompaniment and this must include a sensation of familiarity which makes the recalled item recognizable as a true reproduction of a previous event.

III. Temporal Lobe Fits

Structures in the temporal lobes of the brain are certainly concerned with the emotional accompaniments of recall as is indicated by the remarkable and unique sensations produced by certain focal fits originating in one or other temporal lobe. Focal fits originating in the brain are well known to caricature the normal functions of the region affected and in certain instances of temporal lobe epilepsy intense sensations of familiarity occur—the so-called *déjà vu* sensation, which probably represents an essential facet of recall.

Further, complex hallucinations of vision, hearing, taste, or smell may occur in temporal lobe fits. From the physiological point of view, hallucinations are distorted memories, and it is of great importance that complex hallucinations from temporal lobe lesions may affect almost any sense, for this provides further indication that we are here dealing with a system which is intimately associated with many brain storage systems. Indeed some patients with temporal lobe lesions experience epileptic episodes of forced thinking of a familiar event.

Another feature of certain instances of temporal lobe epilepsy is the occurrence of periods of automatic behaviour for which the patient has subsequently no recollection of events. During this period both memorizing and recall are inactivated.

Unilateral temporal lobectomies for the relief of seizures have provided more evidence for the localization of different aspects of memory function. Work at the Montreal Neurological Institute has suggested that the left temporal lobe "contributes to the rapid understanding and subsequent retention of verbally expressed ideas" while the minor temporal lobe "appears to be more critically involved in perceptual than in verbal skills" (Milner, 1958). This *dichotomy* has also emerged in the Oxford study (unpublished work) of the effects of penetrating missile brain wounds. The group of patients with left-sided lesions are consistently less efficient than the group with right hemisphere lesions in all tasks involving verbal memory and learning but are more efficient in tests of visual memory and visuo-spatial function.

The limbic system is therefore closely concerned in adding to the memory store throughout the brain and it may well be relevant that, under experimental conditions, afferents arriving at the hippocampus cause prolonged and repeated activity, such as might well reflect a repetitive neuronal activity involved in memorizing (Green and Petsche, 1961). The physiology of recall seems also to be intimately concerned with the hippocampal system and yet in Korsakoff's syndrome the memories which are preserved and can be recalled must have been laid down originally with the aid of a memorizing mechanism which is now completely out of action.

Talland's experimental study (1964) of the memory impairment shown by Korsakoff patients has suggested that there are at least two functional deficits, one affecting registration and the other recall. These defects have been related to "premature termination of the on-going process"— impairment to a neural mechanism sustaining mental function. Damage to the mechanism results in the premature termination of registration before the input is embedded in pre-existing systems of mnemonic storage and in failure to recall because of inadequate search or the premature retrieval of incorrect items. This wider conception of both reduced activation and premature closure of function is of interest in that it would account for other perceptual and *cognitive* defects associated with amnesic syndromes and with other neurological conditions in which impairment of memory function presents as a salient feature.

IV. Old Age

In old age there is a notable difficulty in the ability to recall old memories, such as the names of friends, but it is by no means clear whether this difficulty is usually due to a weakening of "recalling mechanisms" or of memory traces—presumably they both weaken and decay sooner or later. Indeed we have little evidence that these two aspects of memory should be considered physiologically distinct. In 1890, William James suggested that "at all times proper names are harder to recollect than those of general properties and classes of things" . . . because they are not so well organized, that is, they have fewer associations and therefore "fewer paths of recall" (James, 1950).

However, a very characteristic difficulty concerns the learning of new material. This difficulty increases with age (Welford, 1956) and is gross in senility, as illustrated in the work of Inglis (1965) and others. Observations in the clinic suggest that immediate memory span, measured by the serial reproduction of a few unrelated items, shows no significant decrease with age. However, short-term storage capacity declines with age in tasks demanding divided attention, simultaneous processing or extending the retention span. Experimental work confirms that age brings increasing vulnerability to the causes of forgetting— trace decay (Fraser, 1958) and interference, i.e. distracting activity (Broadbent and Heron, 1962). Fraser's report on teachers aged 18–29 and 30–55 supports the clinical observations: "It appears that the span of immediate memory is the same for the two age groups, but that the rate of decay of immediate memory tends to increase with age." However, verbal skills, vocabulary in particular, are fairly constant, suggesting that old linguistic skills and memories are relatively impervious to the neuro-physiological changes occurring with age.

V. Observations by the Neurosurgeon

Dr Penfield's name (see Penfield and Jasper, 1954) is especially associated with the surgical study of focal epileptic fits associated with perhaps some complex hallucination or forced thought or feeling, and he has reproduced many such sensations by electrically stimulating the patient's temporal lobes under local anæsthesia. It must of course be clearly understood that artificially produced sensations of this kind only occur on focal stimulation when there is a very irritable and abnormal condition (due to disease) of the mechanism stimulated. Nevertheless, the effect of focal stimulation adds considerably to the knowledge provided by the spontaneously occurring fit.

Penfield's observations on aphasic symptomatology and cortical stimulation and excision, while not providing evidence in favour of cortical specialization for naming, reading and writing, indicate that any cortical tissue, with the possible exception of Broca's area, can be removed without causing permanent aphasia, a finding with clear implications for theories of verbal memories and linguistic storage. Of theoretical interest are his references to the "ganglionic equivalent of a word" and "ganglionic equivalent of a concept", inferences which may eventually be relevant to theoretical models of linguistic behaviour (Morton, 1964).

VI. A Dynamic Process

Further information regarding memory processes is provided by a study of the amnesic accompaniments of cerebral concussion or of electric convulsion therapy (E.C.T.). The phenomenon of retrograde amnesia (R.A.) is of special interest in this connexion.

After head injury which has caused loss of consciousness, or after E.C.T., the patient almost invariably finds he is unable to remember what happened during at least a short period prior to the injury. As far as cerebral commotion is concerned, this period may be just a few seconds, or it may extend for minutes, hours, or even days, but it is clearly some inactivation of a physiological mechanism (presumably repetitive), which demands brain normality for a certain period in order to achieve the establishment of a memory trace. It has been reported that sleep induced after learning (evidence reviewed by Woodworth and Schlosberg, 1963), drugs (Summerfield and Steinberg, 1957) or even sensory deprivation (Grissom, Snedfeld and Vernon, 1962) may improve retention, whereas the retention of material learned before E.C.T. is adversely affected by such treatments (Cronholm and Molander, 1961; Zubin and Barrera, 1940). The latter authors' finding that recent associations lost their superiority over remote ones after E.C.T., and that recall was significantly poorer although learning was not affected, is of interest in this context. Further evidence concerning the importance of "consolidation" of the memory trace has been comprehensively reviewed by Deutsch (1962) and can be inferred from animal experiments (Chow and Survis, 1958), in which once learned habits or memories were shown to persist, despite neo-cortical ablation.

The longer periods of retrograde amnesia extending for perhaps thirty minutes or more tend to be connected with the more severe injuries, and it is of particular importance that during recovery from traumatic confusion remote memories appear first. The patient, for example, at a certain stage may consider himself to be some years younger than he actually is and the date to be some years previous to the real date. This leads to many remarkable situations in which the patient thinks he is still living in a place he left two or three years ago. As recovery progresses the period of retrograde amnesia shrinks towards the present day; the things that were done during the days, hours or minutes preceding the injury are the last to return. Here there is a remarkable relative vulnerability of the more recent memories. This vulnerability applies also to skills acquired shortly before severe injury, and these may be permanently lost (Russell, 1959).

Curiously enough, if the patient is seen within a few minutes of the injury while in a state of traumatic confusion, he may occasionally give information about the injury which later is completely lost (Russell and Nathan, 1946). This seems comparable to the capacity of the person with a Korsakoff's syndrome to repeat digits very quickly after they are presented although a few minutes later he may not even remember the tests being carried out.

It is evident therefore that the duration of retrograde amnesia tends to increase with the severity of brain commotion and tends to shrink during the stages of recovery, and that after severe head injury, memory of events and skills acquired in the days immediately preceding the injury may be permanently lost.

These clinical observations indicate that memorizing is a dynamic process which probably continues for long after the original event, and that the arrest of cerebral activity by injury or E.C.T. has most effect on the most recent events. This is a vital aspect of the physiology of remembering and is supported by animal experiment (Gerard, 1961). These clinical observations therefore suggest a picture of *alerted perception* activating a driving system in the limbic system, which, if allowed to continue even for a second or two, will establish a fairly firm memory trace available for later recall.

This conception is compatible with the occasional occurrence during recovery from cerebral commotion of hallucinations regarding some genuine facet of the accident, such as that of a galloping horse (Russell, 1935; Russell and Nathan, 1946); the hallucination may appear on several occasions during early convalescence. In these instances it may be supposed that *alerted perception* is able to continue for a short time without help from the limbic system, and in support of this view these hallucinations appear during mental relaxation without any feeling of fear or any other affective reaction. The patient with Korsakoff's syndrome often confuses false and true recollections and this also occurs after head injuries and may lead to false accusations regarding the cause of an accident. In this situation it may be supposed that the feeling of familiarity which is a part of accurate recalling may be activated falsely: this interesting phenomenon is not reported in patients who have had bilateral hippocampal excision. On the other hand, the processes of false recognition seem to be very active during dreaming and in the terrifying hallucinations experienced by patients with mental disease. One might imagine some confusion in this system in persons subject to pathological lying where there seems to be a hopeless confusion between truth and imagination. All these examples add to our knowledge of the physiological processes involved in adding to the memory store.

As has been indicated, there is a current tendency to suppose that memory traces originally may represent repeated activity in a neuronal net, but may then become dependent on coding within molecules of RNA. Clinical observations, however, such as those described here, suggest that active repetitive processes may be involved in memorizing and also in strengthening certain memories with the passage of time. This suggests that remote and recent memories are very similar in regard to the physiological mechanisms concerned, as though the changes involved were more dependent on synaptic alterations than on changes in the bodies of the nerve cells and, if this is so, that they are probably maintained by rhythmical activity which is a feature of all neurons.

There is, therefore, no fundamental need to suppose that recent and remote memories employ different physiological mechanisms. Indeed, there is some recent experimental evidence to suggest that certain aspects of short-term memory function are consistent with those of long-term memory (Wickelgren, 1965), findings which may imply similar neurophysiological correlates.

VII. Focal Lesions in Man

In contrast to Lashley's (1929) observations on rats, the study of various anomalies in man indicate that certain aspects of physical and mental activity are particularly dependent on the integrity of certain limited regions of the cerebral hemispheres. Indeed, the localization of function appears to be far more specialized in man than in any other species, although, of course, the tests that can be used in man as regards perception are vastly more complex than is ever feasible in animal experiment.

In general it may be concluded that memories concerned with any aspect of perception and the corresponding afferent pathways require the integrity of regions of the brain closely related to the receiving cortex of the afferent systems concerned.

Thus, motor skills (e.g. swimming) are preserved remarkably well after decades without practice, and yet a deep lesion of the left parietal lobe may produce an apraxia which destroys such skills.

A man who lost a leg was free of all pain for 20 years. He then developed circulatory troubles in the stump and this immediately provoked sensation referred to the toes of the leg he had lost so long ago. The painful afferent up the sciatic nerve aroused memories in relation to the sensory cortex which had been largely dormant for 20 years. In such cases a lesion of the opposite parietal lobe may abolish phantom sensations by destroying the body-image mechanism involved in memories of the missing limb.

Bilateral destruction of the visual or auditory cortex produces, respectively, complete blindness or deafness; but bilateral lesions of certain areas near these regions may cause an inability to interpret visual or auditory activity and present a vast variety of parietal syndromes with their various agnosias and apraxias (Critchley, 1953; Brain, 1961). In man, of course, the development of the language function involves the localization of function in the dominant hemisphere. Unilateral lesions may thus produce agnosias only for the verbal aspect of the afferent system involved, so that there may be isolated word-deafness, or word-blindness, or apraxia for the production of speech. It is quite clear that the areas of the speech territory which produce these isolated anomalies are quite separate and distinct from one another

(Russell and Espir, 1961). Further, at some time we all experience difficulty in remembering a word or the name of an acquaintance; this difficulty may become catastrophic as a result of quite a small lesion in the speech territory of the dominant hemisphere.

All these functions are intimately concerned with learning and with memory, and yet they are individually disorganized by small highly-localized lesions in a particular part of the brain. There is no evidence, however, that *small* areas of the cortex are specially concerned in such syndromes, rather is there a failure of communication due to tract destruction below the cortex. Thus, lesions of the angular gyrus are often related to agnostic syndromes, whereas it seems clear that it is the tracts underlying this area of the brain which are particularly concerned.

VIII. Mechanisms of Recovery

A study of brain wounds incurred in World War II (see Russell and Espir, 1961) indicates that young people have very remarkable powers of recovery after severe brain wounds, and that striking recoveries may also occur after partial destruction of the spinal cord. Severed neurons do not regenerate, but all parts of the central nervous system seem to be plastic and capable of reorganization. The striking recovery that often continues for years after a brain wound which had caused perhaps severe aphasia, must depend on a reorganization of the surviving neurons. Determined practice, effort and encouragement achieve surprising results, especially in the young.

The part played by communication with the opposite (less damaged) cerebral hemisphere in recovery is of great interest in the light of the experimental work of Myers (1956); this is especially important in relation to recovery from aphasia due to severe injury of the dominant hemisphere. For example, a lesion of the left parieto-occipital region may cause complete division of the optic radiation with complete loss of the right field of vision and alexia. Macular visual acuity remains full in these cases even though visual afferents only reach the brain via the *right* optic radiation. The subsequent partial recovery of reading ability probably depends on the integrity of commissural fibres, for the visual information must be "processed" and perhaps led across to the left hemisphere via the corpus callosum for its interpretation into language. From this point of view, the integrity of the commissural fibres may be of first importance, as Myers (1956) found in his experiments and as Geschwindt and Caplan (1962) have emphasized.

It will thus be apparent that careful observations in the clinic have a part to play in adding to existing knowledge of brain mechanisms and in suggesting further lines of research.

References

Barbizet, J. (1963), *J. Neurol. Neurosurg. Psychiat.*, **26**, 127.
Brain, W. R. (1961), *Speech Disorders: Aphasia, Apraxia and Agnosia*, Butterworth, London.
Broadbent, D. E. and Heron, A. (1962), *Brit. J. Psychol.*, **53**, 189.
Chow, K. L. and Survis, J. (1958), *Arch. Neurol. Psychiat.* (*Chic.*), **79**, 640.
Conrad, R. and Hille, B. A. (1958), *Canad. J. Psychol.*, **12**, 1.
Critchley, M. (1953), *The Parietal Lobes*, Arnold, London.
Cronholm, B. and Molander, L. (1961), *Acta. psychiat.* (*Kbh.*), **36**, 83.
Deutsch, J. A. (1962), *Ann. Rev. Physiol.*, **24**, 259.
Fraser, D. C. (1958), *Nature* (*Lond.*), **182**, 1163.
Gerard, R. W. (1961), In *Brain Mechanisms and Learning*, pp. 29 and 183, Blackwell, Oxford.
Geschwindt, N. and Caplan, E. (1962), *Neurology* (*Minneap.*), **12**, 675.
Glickman, S. E. (1961), *Psychol. Bull.*, **58**, 218.
Green, J. D. and Petsche, H. (1961), *Electroenceph. clin. Neurophysiol.*, **13**, 847.
Grissom, R. J., Snedfeld, P. and Vernon, J. (1962), *Science*, **138**, 429.
Hebb, D. O. (1949), *The Organization of Behaviour*, Wiley, New York.
Inglis, J. (1965), *Behaviour, Aging and the Nervous System*, (Edited by A. T. Welford, and J. E. Birren,), C. C. Thomas, Springfield, Ill.
James, W. (1950), *The Principles of Psychology*, Constable, London.
Lashley, K. S. (1929), *Brain Mechanisms and Intelligence*, Univ. Chicago Press, Chicago.
Magoun, H. W. (1954), *Brain Mechanisms and Consciousness*, Blackwell, Oxford.
Mahut, H. (1957), *Amer. J. Psychol.*, **12**, 466.
Milner, B. (1958), *Proc. Ass. Res. nerv. ment. Dis.*, **36**, 244.
Moruzzi, G. and Magoun, H. W. (1949), *Electroenceph. clin. Neurophysiol.*, **1**, 455.
Morton, J. (1964), *Language and Speech*, 7, 40.
Myers, R. E. (1956), *Brain*, **79**, 358.
Penfield, W. and Jasper, H. (1954), *Epilepsy and the Functional Anatomy of the Human Brain*, Churchill, London.
Rose, F. C. and Symonds, C. P. (1960), *Brain*, **83**, 195.
Russell, W. Ritchie (1935), *Lancet*, **2**, 762.
Russell, W. Ritchie (1959), *Brain: Memory: Learning*, Clarendon Press, Oxford.
Russell, W. Ritchie (1964), *Brit. med. J.*, **2**, 403.
Russell, W. Ritchie and Espir, M. (1961), *Traumatic Aphasia*, Oxford University Press, London.
Russell, W. Ritchie and Nathan, P. (1946), *Brain*, **69**, 280.
Scoville, W. B. and Milner, B. (1957), *J. Neurol. Neurosurg. Psychiat.*, **20**, 11.
Summerfield, A. and Steinberg, H. (1957), *Quart. J. exp. Psychol.*, **9**, 146.
Talland, G. A. (1965), *Deranged Memory*, Academic Press, London.
Welford, A. T. (1956), In *Experimental Research on Aging*, (Edited by F. Versar), Basel.
Wickelgren, W. A. (1965), *J. verb. Learn. verb. Behav.*, **4**, 53.
Williams, M. and Pennybacker, J. B. (1954), *J. Neurol. Neurosurg. Psychiat.*, **17**, 115.
Williams, M. and Smith, H. V. (1954), *J. Neurol. Neurosurg. Psychiat.*, **17**, 173.
Woodworth, R. S. and Schlosberg, H. (1963), In *Experimental Psychology*, p. 768, Holt, Rinehart & Winston, New York.
Zubin, J. and Barrera, S. E. (1941), *Proc. Soc. exp. Biol.* (*N.Y.*), **48**, 596.

Some Aspects of the Disorders of Memory due to Brain Damage

J. B. Brierley

I. Introduction

Some deterioration in the ability to remember the events of everyday life is a well known failing in perhaps the majority of elderly people. In contrast to this impairment in what will be called the process of memorizing (i.e. the ability to retain and to recall new sensory material), the recall of the events of childhood and early adult life is often well preserved. Thus eventually, some old people might be said to live almost entirely in the past. However, a disturbance of memory of this type and in varying degree is but one of several that may be encountered as symptoms of certain diseases of the brain.

The purpose of this brief review is to discuss some of the information obtained from the examination of the human brain by neuropathologists. This has led to the conclusion that the retention and recall of any sensory impression or experience depend on the structural integrity of certain small and relatively well-defined portions of the brain. That is not to say that because damage in these structures produces some defect in memorizing, this function itself must reside within them, any more than the blindness produced by severence of the optic nerve justifies the conclusion that vision is located within the nerve. The various disorders of memory that occur in cases of hysteria and of functional psychosis (mental illnesses in which there is no evidence of brain damage) will not be considered here.

Before discussing the nature and the sites of brain damage that can be correlated with a disturbance of memorizing, the terms used to describe these disturbances must be examined. The two that are most frequently used in clinical practice are a defect of "recent", "immediate" or "short-term memory" or "memory for recent events" and a defect of "remote" or "long-term memory" or "memory for remote events". Unfortunately neither of these terms has been defined with precision. Thus a failure to retain and to recall new sensory material (such as a series of digits) for longer than two or three minutes has been called, with some justification, a defect of "short-term memory" or of "memory for recent events". Other clinicians have used the same term to describe patients whose retention and recall of new material lasts for as long as two or three weeks. In fact, the boundary in terms of time between recent and remote has not been defined and it can only be said that "long-term memory" usually refers to the events of childhood and early adult life.

The use and the significance of these two terms must be considered in the perspective of the fate of all the sensory impressions and experiences of the present moment. It is evident that the greater part of these will not be accessible to normal recall for more than a few minutes or even seconds. Progressively smaller fractions will be retained for progressively longer periods and only a minority are destined to become the "remote memories" of, say, 30 years hence. Thus selection of material for storage and the apparently widely differing periods of storage are central features of human memory.

It is only when the territory of the "normally forgotten" begins to expand at the expense of the "normally remembered" (as judged by comparison with a person's previous memory function and with our conception of the normal) that a defect of memory can be said to exist. At the start and throughout the course of the disability, if it is progressive, selectivity is usually demonstrable since important and particularly emotionally coloured material tends to be preserved, while the less important and the emotionally neutral is not.

While accurate assessment and, if possible, quantitative assessment of memory is the task and goal of the psychologist, it must be appreciated that psychological tests in current use are well suited to the characterization and measurement of a disorder of recent memory in which the retention span is of the order of minutes. In such cases, the ability to retain and reproduce a series of digits or letters or the content of a paragraph, can be scored with precision. When, however, the reduced retention span is a matter of days or even weeks, the presentation of test material would be separated from the test itself by a considerable interval. During this time the patient would have returned to his ward or to his home where he would have been subjected to diverse uncontrollable external influences which could affect to an unknown extent his ability to recall when tested. In such cases, the evidence for some failure in memorizing comes almost entirely from the patient himself (if he retains insight into his condition), his relatives and his immediate social contacts. A disability defined in this way, although less incapacitating, is no less real than one in which retention, reduced to a few minutes, can be given quantitative expression on the basis of psychological test scores.

A third term employed to describe a particular disorder of memory is "retrograde amnesia". This term is relatively precise in that it defines

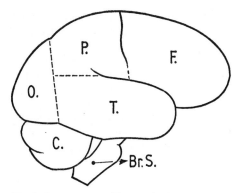

Fig. 1. Outer aspect of human brain.

F = frontal lobe; T = temporal lobe; P = parietal lobe; O = occipital lobe; C = cerebellum; Br. S = brain stem.

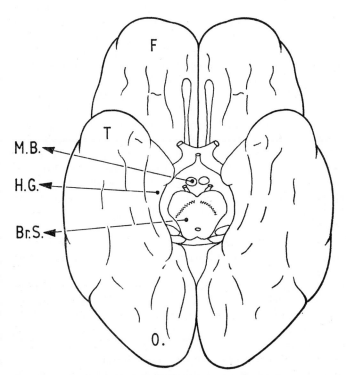

Fig. 2. Lower aspect of brain with brain stem and cerebellum removed.

F = frontal lobe; O = occipital lobe; T = temporal lobe; M.B. = mamillary body; Br.S. = brain stem cut across; H.G. = hippocampal gyrus.

a period of time before an accident or an illness for the events of which the patient has either no recollection at all or has the ability to recall only a few.

There is now a considerable body of evidence to show that an impairment of memory for recent events, and frequently for some period of retrograde amnesia, are prominent symptoms of damage within two separate but interconnected regions of the brain. These are the hypothalamus and the temporal lobes and the evidence upon which this conclusion is based will now be considered. The major features of the outer and lower aspects of the human brain are shown in Figs. 1 and 2.

II. The Hypothalamus

In 1887 the Russian psychiatrist Korsakoff described a mental disorder or psychosis that has borne his name ever since. The affected subject is usually confused, is unaware of his whereabouts and of the hour, the day, the month and even the year (disorientation in space and time). He may be subject to hallucinations and eventually become delirious and comatose. If some recovery takes place or if the psychosis is less severe, a disturbance of memory is apparent. This consists of two of the disorders of memory that have already been defined. There is firstly a retrograde amnesia extending backwards in time for as much as a year before the illness: for the events of this period, recollection is either completely impossible or limited to a few experiences. If appropriate treatment is begun this period of retrograde amnesia may contract to a variable extent. The second type of memory disorder characteristic of the psychosis is some failure to retain and recall recent events. In its most severe form no new sensory material (of auditory, verbal or any other type) can be retained and reproduced after more than one or two minutes. This striking failure to memorize recent events often contrasts sharply with the patient's ability to recall with fair accuracy the remote events of childhood.

A further feature of the psychosis is confabulation, which implies that the patient will recount fictitious events spontaneously as well as in reply to questions.

Many of the patients exhibiting Korsakoff's psychosis are alcoholics in a poor state of nutrition but, as Korsakoff himself was well aware, the psychosis occurs in a variety of other clinical settings. These include cancer of the stomach and intestinal tract, severe and protracted vomiting, certain types of anæmia, poisoning by certain metals and in some instances of deficient oxygen supply to the brain.

The pathological alterations in the brains of two alcoholics had, in fact, been described by Wernicke in 1881 and similar changes were present in a third case which was one of poisoning by sulphuric acid. Nevertheless the relationship between this pathology in the brain and the psychosis was not realized by Korsakoff who considered that the damage lay in the nerve fibres of the white matter beneath the cerebral cortex. Gudden (1896) was the first to appreciate the true relationship and to point out that the mamillary bodies (Fig. 3) in the posterior part of the hypothalamus were consistently involved. Although a single case of Korsakoff's psychosis in which the alterations were confined to the two mamillary bodies was described by Rémy (1942), the recent careful

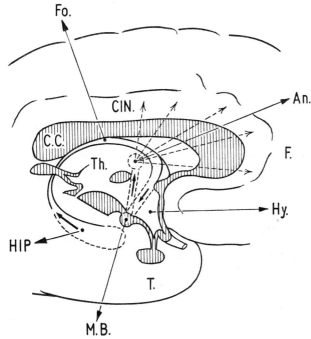

Fig. 3. Mid-line section of left cerebral hemisphere. From the hippocampus (HIP), the fornix (Fo) curves round to the mamillary body (M.B.) whence the mamillo-thalamic tract leads to the anterior nucleus (An) of the thalamus (Th) which projects to the cingulate gyrus (CIN).

Hy = hypothalamus; C.C. = corpus callosum; F = frontal lobe; T = temporal lobe.

neuropathological study of 54 cases of the psychosis by Adams, Collins and Victor (1962) suggests that thalamic as well as mamillary body damage is essential for the production of the memory disorder typical of this psychosis. Within the altered portions of the brain, there is a variable loss of nerve cells, production of new capillaries and glial cells (astrocytes and microglia) and frequently small hæmorrhages.

The factor responsible for the appearance of Korsakoff's psychosis and the pathology just described in conditions as diverse as alcoholism, gastric cancer and severe vomiting has been shown to be a lack of or a failure to absorb one constituent of the vitamin B complex—B_1 or thiamine. This was first established when the typical alterations in the brain were brought about by feeding a thiamine-deficient diet to pigeons (Alexander, 1939); later, similar results were obtained for cats (Ferraro and Roizin, 1941). This discovery led to the possibility of treating patients with Korsakoff's psychosis by injecting the vitamin in adequate amounts. It is interesting to note that if treatment is begun early enough, many features of the psychosis may disappear and there may be some improvement in the retrograde amnesia. The defect in memory for recent events usually remains although occasionally there is some degree of improvement.

III. The Temporal Lobes

The original observation suggesting that, in man, the temporal lobes and particularly the structures along their inner borders, are concerned in the process of memorizing was that of the Russian neurophysiologist von Bechterew in 1900. He reported, very briefly, a patient who had a striking defect of memory as well as apathy for several years before his death. A defect of memory particularly, for recent events, was attributed to bilateral damage in the temporal lobes in the single case described by Glees and Griffiths (1952). In this case the damage appeared to involve the hippocampus (Fig. 3) and more or less of the adjacent regions so that precise delineation of the structure or structures essential for normal memorizing was not possible.

Further information on this last point was provided, inadvertently, by the results of neurosurgical procedures designed in the first place to cure or alleviate certain cases of severe mental illness (including schizophrenia) and later, cases of temporal lobe epilepsy. In the latter condition the seizure is often heralded by an aura or warning consisting of the awareness of an odour or of a brief train of events that appear familiar at the time (sensation of *déjà vu*) or both. These auras are known to be symptoms of some abnormality within the deeper portions of the temporal lobes. The aura may be followed by a transient loss of contact with the surroundings or by a typical major convulsion (grand mal seizure). The purpose of surgery in such patients is to remove the diseased tissue which is believed to be the source of the seizure.

In the early days of this type of surgery, the American neurosurgeon Scoville (1954), removed tissue from the inner margin of both temporal lobes in nine patients and the results of the operation were assessed and reported by Scoville and Milner (1957). Eight were cases of severe mental illness and one was a severe epileptic. There was little effect in cases of mental illness but the frequency of seizures was reduced in the epileptic patient. There was ". . . one striking and totally unexpected behavioural result: a grave loss of recent memory in those cases in which the medial temporal lobe resection was so extensive as to involve the major portion of the hippocampal complex bilaterally." In some cases there was also a retrograde amnesia for a period of up to three years before the operation. Intelligence and the ability to recall the events of childhood were preserved. In general, the impairment of memory for recent events was considered to be proportional to the amount of hippocampal tissue removed. When only the tips of the temporal lobes including the amygdaloid nuclei had been removed, memory was unaffected. The conclusion was reached that the hippocampus and the related hippocampal gyrus (together forming the hippocampal formation) of both sides are necessary for the memorizing of recent events. It must be noted, however, that confirmation of the precise extent of the surgical removal of tissue by pathological examination of the brain has not yet been reported in any of these cases.

In subsequent attempts to treat temporal lobe epilepsy, surgeons have heeded the warning explicitly given in the above report and have limited the operation to the removal of some fraction of one temporal lobe only. Improved diagnostic methods, and the use of the electroencephalogram (EEG) in particular, have shown that in many cases the major abnormality lies on one side. The portion of the temporal lobe that is usually removed in these operations includes the tip of the lobe, part of the amygdaloid nucleus, more or less of the outer surface and part of the inner aspect containing the hippocampus and the hippocampal gyrus.

It was soon apparent that the removal of only one temporal lobe was not without effect upon memory in certain cases. When the lobe on the dominant side (i.e. the left side in a right-handed person) is removed there is a mild impairment in the ability to remember purely verbal material (Meyer and Yates, 1955; Penfield and Milner, 1958). When the lobe of the non-dominant side is removed there is some defect in the rapid visual identification of objects (Penfield and Milner, 1958). A more general defect of memory for recent events consequent on the removal of the non-dominant temporal lobe has been reported by Serafetinides and Falconer (1962) who also drew attention to the appearance, after the operation, of an abnormal EEG focus (suggestive of abnormal tissue) in the opposite temporal lobe. In 7 out of 34 patients who had undergone unilateral temporal lobectomy and had been followed up for a period of 2–9 years, evidence of impaired memory for recent events was obtained from the patients themselves and from their close relatives or friends. In no instance was the disability incapacitating; and it is important to note that it had not been revealed by formal psychometric tests, the results of which were normal. A defect of memory of this type differs only in severity from the gross disorder of memorizing that followed the removal of the inner parts of both temporal lobes by Scoville. Further, as this is a defect of memory for recent events, it is clearly the equivalent of that which has already been described as a feature of Korsakoff's psychosis.

Within the temporal lobe, the structures which when damaged or removed on both sides, result in some failure to retain and recall recent events, are the hippocampus and the closely related hippocampal gyrus. The participation of the tip of the lobe, its outer aspect and the amygdaloid nucleus in the process of memorizing seems to be unimportant, as it is known that this process is unimpaired by the bilateral removal of these regions alone.

From these considerations of Korsakoff's psychosis and its underlying neuropathology and from those of surgery and disease of the temporal lobes, it may be concluded that the portions of the brain apparently essential for the conversion of the experiences of the present into the remembered past are the two mamillary bodies of the posterior hypothalamus, the medial portions of both thalami, the two hippocampi and the two hippocampal gyri. Before the relevant information concerning the structure and the nerve fibre connexions of these regions of the brain is reviewed, mention must be made of the fact that a defect of memory for recent events can be a symptom of a large number of different pathological processes involving some or all of these structures. These processes include tumours compressing or invading the thalamus and hypothalamus, some types of inflammation of the brain (encephalitis) which tend to involve its under surface on either side of the mid-line, and disease of the blood vessels which may interfere with the blood supply to the structures in question. All these conditions however, in themselves, provide little precise information as to the location of the regions of the brain concerned with memorizing. They have been reviewed elsewhere (Brierley, 1961; Adams, Collins and Victor, 1962).

IV. Neuro-Anatomical Aspects

The mamillary bodies (Figs. 2 and 3)   These paired structures form small pea-like protuberances on either side of the mid-line on the under surface of the cerebral hemispheres and in the posterior part of the hypothalamus. Their principal incoming (afferent) fibres are derived from the hippocampus and run within the fornix (described below). Others enter from the brain stem and from some of the adjacent hypothalamic nuclei. The principal outgoing (efferent) pathway is the mamillo-thalamic tract which ends in the anterior group of nuclei of the thalamus.

Relevant nuclei of the thalamus   The thalami are paired structures lying deep within the hemispheres on either side of the mid-line and above the hypothalamus.

1. *Anterior nuclei* (Fig. 3)   The principal afferents come from the

mamillary bodies as the mamillo-thalamic tract. The efferent fibres project to the cingulate gyrus (Fig. 3), a strip of cerebral cortex lying on the inner aspect of each hemisphere just above the compact mass of transversely running fibres which connects them (the corpus callosum). 2. *Dorsomedial nuclei*   These nuclei lie within the thalami on either side of the mid-line. Their afferent fibres are derived from the hypo-thalamus and from other thalamic nuclei. Their efferent fibres project to the greater part of the cortex of the frontal lobes. 3. *The pulvinar*   This name is given to the convex posterior portion of the thalamus. Its afferent fibres come from the pathways of auditory and visual sensation and its efferent fibres project to large areas of the cortex of the temporal and occipital lobes.

The amygdaloid nuclei   These large nuclei lie in the deepest portions of the temporal lobes near their tips. Their afferents are derived from numerous sources including the olfactory pathway, some hypothalamic nuclei and possibly from the pathway of visceral sensation. The efferent fibres run to the hypothalamus.

The hippocampus and the hippocampal gyrus   These two structures will be considered together because there is no sharp line of demarcation between them, they are closely interconnected and in surgery of the temporal lobe they are usually removed together.

The hippocampus (Fig. 3) consists of a strip of cortex made up of three layers of nerve cells, whereas the remainder of the cerebral cortex is made up of six layers. It is folded into the temporal lobe from its inner surface so that the deepest aspect of the strip bulges into the ventricular cavity of the lobe and its lower edge is continuous with the hippocampal gyrus which is the visible inner border of the temporal lobe. In lower vertebrates such as the rodents, the hippocampus forms a part of the "smell brain" (rhinencephalon) but in man there is no evidence that it receives direct fibres from the olfactory nerves. The main source of its afferent fibres is the adjacent hippocampal gyrus while others come from the anterior part of the hypothalamus, the hippo-campus of the opposite side and probably from the brain stem reticular system. This is a system of collateral or branching fibres from the main sensory pathways which enters the thalamus and hypothalamus and is believed to assist in the control of the level of consciousness. The principal efferent pathway is the fornix which takes a C-shaped course, first backwards, then upwards and forwards around the posterior aspect of the thalamus and finally downwards to end in the mamillary bodies. Before these are reached some fibres are given off and end in the anterior hypothalamus, parts of the thalamus and the upper brain stem.

The afferent connexions of the hippocampal gyrus are poorly known but include fibres from the olfactory pathway, the brain stem and possibly from several areas of the cerebral cortex.

V. Discussion

From the neuro-anatomical data that have been presented and summarized in Fig. 3, it would appear that a continuous pathway can be traced along the afferent fibres from the hippocampal gyrus into the hippocampus itself and through its efferent pathway, the fornix, to the mamillary bodies. From these the mamillo-thalamic tract leads to the anterior nuclear group of the thalamus which projects finally to the cingulate gyrus. The latter is one of the cortical regions known to be connected with the hippocampal gyrus so that, at first glance, a continuous "circuit" might be said to exist and, in fact, the name "limbic system" has been given to the whole group of structures and their connexions. It has been suggested that they are concerned with the receipt of sensations from the viscera and the elaboration of the emotions.

It has already been shown that a defect of memory for recent events can be the result of damage in either the two mamillary bodies together with the medial and pulvinar nuclei of the thalami, or in the two hippocampi and the hippocampal gyri. It is surprising therefore that with the exception of one case, bilateral division of the fornix, which is the largest apparent connecting link between the two groups of structures, has failed to produce a significant alteration in memory. This observation alone suggests that it is premature to regard the chain of structures linked by the fornices as a unitary system subserving the process of memorizing.

The information already presented has defined the structures concerned with the process of memorizing, and may also throw some light on certain aspects of the nature of this process itself. While damage within these structures can prevent the normal establishment of a new sensory experience as a permanent "structural" memory trace or "engram", it is believed that a definitive period of time is required for this establishment or consolidation to take place. This conclusion is based on the observation that the recall of a new sensory impression can be impaired if an electrically induced epileptic seizure occurs within a few hours of the receipt of the impression (Cronholm and Mollander, 1957, 1959). The induced seizure was found to be most effective in impairing the recall of test words and numbers when it occurred soon after they were presented and was almost without effect if delayed for a few hours. It is probable that in everyday life there is no single "consolidation time" that is applicable to all new sensory material, since that which is important and emotionally charged tends to be more rapidly embedded than that which is emotionally neutral or unimportant.

The existence of some period of retrograde amnesia after damage in the mamillary and hippocampal regions has been regarded by Milner (1962) and Adams *et al.* (1962) as evidence that the period of consolidation or embedding may be one of months or even years rather than one of hours. On the other hand, it would seem that the shrinkage or even the disappearance of a period of retrograde amnesia in some cases (e.g. encephalitis—Rose and Symonds, 1960; Adams, Collins and Victor, 1962; head injury—Russell and Nathan, 1946) would suggest that the defect was one of recall rather than consolidation.

It was pointed out in the introduction that selection of the material to be consolidated as an engram is a feature of normal memory and one which is retained to some extent even when the mamillary and hippocampal regions are damaged. This fact suggests that the process of selection (or filtration) of new sensory material may not be a function of these regions themselves but of some other region, perhaps in the upper brain stem or thalamus, where the total sensory input can be compared and correlated with stored experience, and its importance, familiarity and emotional content assessed.

Attention has also been drawn to the widely different periods of normal storage of new sensory material (as judged by ability to recall), ranging from seconds to a lifetime. In this context the report of Serafetinides and Falconer (1962) has provided evidence that when some damage exists within both hippocampal regions, the span of retention and recall, although reduced, may be as long as weeks or even months. In such cases there seems little justification for regarding the underlying defect as one of fixation or consolidation alone, not only because the duration of this process is not known for all categories of sensory impressions, but because the presentation of appropriate associations may, in such cases, render possible the recall of material that was apparently forgotten. In view of these arguments it may be unjustifiable to attribute to the mamillary and hippocampal structures a function that is solely one of conversion of new experiences into their remembered engrams. They may well play some role in the process of recall.

There is no convincing evidence that remote memories are formed by a process basically different from recent memories, although the terms "short-term" and "long-term" memory might suggest that there was. It is also becoming apparent that a defect in the process of memorizing can produce a range of reduced retention times extending from a few minutes in a patient with a severe Korsakoff psychosis to weeks and even months in a patient with damage in the temporal lobes.

The clinical and neuropathological evidence which has been presented in summary is also relevant to any hypothesis designed to explain the nature of the process of memorizing, whether framed in biochemical or neurophysiological terms. The essential phenomena that a satisfactory hypothesis must explain are:

1. The selection (or filtration) of new sensory material in a way that is not all-or-none but is according to criteria which include familiarity, importance, and emotional colouring, as assessed by comparison with stored experience.

2. The retention of only a fraction of the sensory input as a permanent trace or engram and the loss of the remainder after widely differing periods of retention.

3. The ability to recall any new material at any time within its span of retention, whether this be minutes or years.

4. The probable role of the mamillary and hippocampal zones as a group of structures which, irrespective of the character of the sensory impression, can determine its ultimate fixation as an engram after periods of fixation or consolidation that may be widely different.

There is, as yet, no satisfactory evidence to indicate in which region of the brain the "engram" may be stored. Penfield and Perot (1963) have presented very extensive evidence to show that stimulation of the outer aspect of the temporal lobes of conscious patients subject to temporal lobe epilepsy can give rise to the recall of what appear to be previous events in the history of the patient. However, this phenomenon has not been reproduced in patients whose temporal lobes are normal, so that there may be no good reason to depart from the view of Lashley (1950) that memories have no precise localization.

In conclusion, it is to be stressed that one unique feature of the memory of man is his ability to make use of the code of number, quality and experience represented by words which, once learned, enables him to communicate with his fellows as a member of society and to have access to its collective experience. The power of speech, (the "second signalling system" of Pavlov) is entirely responsible for man's unique ability to exchange complex experiences with his fellows and to dispense with the uneconomical process of conditioning in its classical sense. A second feature, probably present to some degree in animals, is man's ability to retain and recall a single impression or experience without the necessity of repetition inherent in the process of formal learning. The faculty of speech in its verbal and written forms, together with the ability to retain complex material after a single presentation are essential prerequisites of introspective memory and above all, of abstract thought.

VI. Summary and Conclusions

The nature of the disorders of memory attributable to brain damage, and the terms used to describe them, have been discussed. Although "a defect of memory for recent events" is a valid clinical descriptive term, it is evident that remote and recent memories are formed originally by the same process, to which the term memorizing has been applied.

A defect of memory for recent events can be a symptom of damage in the mamillary bodies and certain thalamic nuclei and is seen typically as a component of Korsakoff's psychosis. An essentially similar disturbance of memorizing can result from damage within the hippo-campal formation of both temporal lobes. Some degree of retrograde amnesia can be a symptom of damage in either region.

The reduced memory span for recent events can range from a few minutes to weeks or months and can then escape detection by formal psychometric tests and can be defined only on the basis of evidence from the patient himself and his immediate social contacts.

The principal connexions of the structures apparently concerned with the process of memorizing have been described briefly. The absence of a defect in this process after bilateral section of the fornix is one reason for hesitancy in describing the whole complex as a unitary system responsible for the consolidation and eventual recall of present events.

References

Adams, R. D., Collins, G. H. and Victor, M. (1962), In *Physiologie de l'Hippocampe. Colloques Internationaux de Centre National de la Recherche Scientifique*, No. 107, p. 273.
Alexander, L. (1939), *Arch. Neurol. Psychiat. (Chic.)*, **42**, 1172.
Bechterew, W. V. von (1900), *Neurol. Cbl.*, **19**, 990.
Brierley, J. B. (1961), *Geront. clin.*, **3**, 97.
Cronholm, B. and Mollander, L. (1957), *Acta psychiat. (Kbh)*, **32**, 280.
Cronholm, B. and Mollander, L. (1959), *Acta psychiat. (Kbh)*, **34**, 18.
Ferraro, A. and Roizin, L. (1941), *Trans. Amer. neurol. Ass.*, **67**, 177.
Glees, P. and Griffiths, H. B. (1952), *Mschr. Psychiat. Neurol.*, **123**, 193.
Gudden, H. (1896), *Arch. Psychiat. Nervenkr.*, **28**, 643.
Korsakoff, S. (1887), *Westnik Psichiatr.*, **4**, No. 2.
Lashley, K. S. (1950), *Symp. Soc. exp. Biol.*, **4**, 454.
Meyer, V. and Yates, A. J. (1955), *J. Neurol. Neurosurg. Psychiat.*, **18**, 44.
Milner, B. (1962), In *Physiologie de l'Hippocampe. Colloques Internationaux de Centre National de la Recherche Scientifique*, No. 107, p. 257.
Penfield, W. and Milner, B. (1958), *Arch. Neurol. Psychiat. (Chic.)*, **79**, 475.
Penfield, W. and Perot, P. (1962), *Brain*, **86**, 595.
Rémy, M. (1942), *Mschr. Psychiat. Neurol.*, **106**, 128.
Rose, F. C. and Symonds, C. P. (1960), *Brain*, **83**, 195.
Russell, W. R. and Nathan, P. W. (1946), *Brain*, **69**, 280.
Scoville, W. B. (1954), *J. Neurosurg.*, **11**, 64.
Scoville, W. B. and Milner, B. (1957), *J. Neurol. Neurosurg. Psychiat.*, **20**, 11.
Serafetinides, E. A. and Falconer, M. A. (1962), *J. Neurol. Neurosurg. Psychiat.*, **25**, 251.
Wernicke, C. (1881), *Lehrbuch der Gehirhkrankheiten*, Bd. 2, p. 229, Fischer, Kassel & Berlin, Deutschland.

The Neurological Basis of Learning

J. H. Gaddum

Anyone who is interested in the activities of individual neurons in the brain would like to form some picture of their relation to the activities of the whole animal. Much work has been done on this topic and it is open to everyone to make his own summary and consider the meaning of the facts.

The speculations made here are an attempt to do this. They are mostly unoriginal and some may appear improbable, but it is possible that one or more may prove the stimulus for further experiment. Various assumptions have been made without evidence and the language of psychology has been confused with that of physiology, and fact with fancy; but it is hoped that this will lead to argument and so to clearer theories. Some of the assumptions may be wrong, but this does not prove that they are all wrong.

I. Models of the Brain

The biological success of animals depends partly on their power to make movements and to adapt these movements in the light of signals coming from the outside world. When the conditions are standardized it is possible to get a constant response to a given signal. This fact led to the belief in the 19th century that a reflex was a mechanical response which did not depend on the previous history of the animal. There is, of course, some truth in this belief, but it is surprising what simple nerve nets can learn from experience.

Von Frisch (1962) has shown that bees can learn that a blue background is associated with food. In this instance the blue colour is the conditioned stimulus, food the unconditioned. Bees can also learn the pathway leading to food and to communicate this information to other bees using the sun as a guide—and the weight of their brain is only about 2·5 mg. *Octopus vulgaris* can learn that some white shapes are signals of danger and will then take appropriate avoiding action (Young, 1961). These facts show that learning may occur in a small organ. Similar learning also occurs in a wide variety of other simple animals (Thorpe, 1963).

It is tempting to suppose that the mechanism which controls behaviour and modifies it in the light of experience has something in common in all animals. The word plastic is applied to nerve nets whose properties are altered by experience and it is thought that the study of plastic nerve nets in simple animals may throw some light on the mode of action of the brains of complex animals. The main seat of the intellect must be a plastic nerve net of some kind, though it is possible to have plasticity without intellect. In the higher mammals intelligence is associated particularly with the cerebral cortex, as the following facts reveal:
1. The species of animal with the most complicated cortex are in general the most intelligent.
2. When the cortex is absent through disease, intelligence is absent too.
3. Extirpation of the whole cortex destroys intelligence.
It does not follow, however, that the cerebral cortex is the only part of the brain where plastic changes occur. Most nerve nets are to some extent plastic and the difference between them is a matter of degree. According to Gastaut and others (see Morrell, 1961) the thalamus and the reticular formation play a major part in the formation of conditioned reflexes.

There has been much speculation about how plastic nerve nets work and various theories have been put forward in the form of models which are thought to resemble real brains. In the early part of this century the brain was thought to be like a telephone exchange in which each sensation was switched through to one particular centre, and each motor act was caused by another particular centre. The function of the brain was to connect these two centres with one another in some way. This theory was taken to imply that each sensation, and each motor act, depended on a localized area of the brain, and would disappear if that area was destroyed. This is true in the sense that visual sensations are analysed in the occipital cortex and that speech commonly depends on a particular part of the motor cortex, but it was found experimentally that localization was less important than had been supposed and that localized destruction of the cerebral cortex did not cause clearly defined losses of function. Lashley (1929) carried out experiments with rats in which various large areas of cerebrum were removed and the rats were tested for their ability to find their way through mazes. He came to the conclusion that the whole cerebrum was equally important for this purpose and that the rat's performance depended only on how much cerebrum was left. He concluded that the whole cerebrum was equipotential. This is an extreme view, but it is now generally agreed that even simple responses depend on the activity of large areas of cerebrum.

Some of the brain models which have been proposed are theoretical. Others have led to the construction of actual mechanical models. For example, Ashby (1954) constructed a model, known as a homeostat, with four units, each containing pivoted magnets, a diode and variable resistances, connected up so that the output from each unit goes to the other three. When one unit is disturbed the other three find new positions of equilibrium.

Grey Walter (1953) was responsible for the construction of various models showing more enterprise than the homeostat, and surprising signs of intelligence. One of these, known as *Machina speculatrix*, looks like a tortoise and runs about on three wheels driven by electric batteries and motors. Instead of an eye, it has a photoelectric cell attached to the steering wheel, which keeps rotating until it points towards a light, when rotation stops and the machine advances towards the light. If the light is too bright the machine avoids it. If two such machines, each carrying its own light, come within sight of one another, they are first of all attracted and then repelled. When one of these machines meets an obstacle it backs away from it and then tries again; it pushes small obstacles out of the way, goes round larger ones and avoids slopes. Eventually, it finds its way to a lighted hutch, where its batteries are recharged, and when this has been done it sets out on another voyage of exploration. This machine shows enterprise, but not intelligence.

A more complicated version was christened *Machina docilis*, because it can learn. It contains a mechanical ear as well as a mechanical eye and, if a whistle is repeatedly followed by a light, the machine learns to associate the two, so that when the combination has been repeated about twenty times it responds to the whistle. It can also learn that a whistle means trouble, so that it behaves as if there was an obstacle in the way. This machine also responds to touch, and may suffer from conflict when the acquired response to touch is different from the acquired response to sound.

Computers have been constructed which act quickly and deal with problems too complex for the ordinary brain (Bowden, 1962). This work has established some of the general principles of information theory and suggested ways in which brains might work, but real knowledge of living brains is likely to depend on more direct studies.

During the years 1930–1940 much was learned about the physiology of cells in the central nervous system. This was summarized by Lorente de No (1939) in an important paper which includes speculations about functions. Various later writers have taken these facts into consideration (Hebb, 1949; Eccles, 1953; Gerard, 1960), and have proposed theories of how nerve cells such as those which are known to exist might be connected together and might act on one another to form a plastic nerve net with properties like those of living brains. These theories will not be discussed in detail here, but the model suggested by Beurle (1957), which developed from a theory proposed by Uttley (1955), is described below in the section dealing with mechanisms. It is based on the theory, proposed by Hebb (1949), that the brain contains a randomly distributed mass of cells with properties like those of some of the cells in the central nervous system. Beurle's calculations led to the conclusion that waves of activity would pass through such a network of cells and that the properties of the network would be altered by the passage of the waves in ways which would be predictable if all the facts were known. In practice the facts are likely to be so complicated that no such prediction could be made.

II. Perception

Sensations reach the central nervous system in the form of electrical impulses in sensory nerves, whose distribution in time and space depend on objects in the outside world. The message which they bring cannot be of any value, even for the formation of the simplest conditioned reflex, until it has been interpreted in terms of ideas formed by experience. This process is sometimes called perception. The word "idea" was originally derived from introspection, and has been much used by philosophers, some of whom have regarded ideas as part of the hereditary structure of the mind. John Locke, who was one of the earliest Fellows of the Royal Society and was closely concerned with the sudden development of scientific thought in the 17th century, took the opposite view. He believed that ideas "are no more born with us than the arts and sciences", but acquired by the experience of each individual. The mind starts without ideas and comes to be furnished with ideas "such as those expressed by the words whiteness, hardness, sweetness, thinking, motion, man, elephant, army, drunkenness and others". All these ideas are furnished by experience. This extreme view had a profound effect on thought and led to a number of interesting conclusions.

Locke (1690) tells how the learned and worthy Mr Molineux sent him a problem: "Suppose a man *born* blind, and now adult, and taught by his *touch* to distinguish between a cube and a sphere of the same metal, and nighly of the same bigness, so as to tell, when he felt one and the other, which is the cube and which the sphere. Suppose then the cube and sphere placed on a table, and the blind man made to see: quære, whether *by his sight, before he touched them,* he could now distinguish and tell which is the globe and which the cube?" To which the acute and judicious proposer answers: "Not. For though he has obtained the experience of how a globe and how a cube affects his touch, yet he has not obtained the experience, that what affects his touch so and so, must affect his sight so and so, or that a protuberant angle in the cube that pressed his hand unequally, shall appear to his eye as it does in the cube." Locke agrees with this thinking gentleman, whom he is proud to call his friend.

This problem has been much discussed by philosophers, and, in the course of time, a great deal of information relating to it has accumulated. This is summarized in a book by von Senden (1940) in which observations on 66 blind persons during the last few centuries are discussed. The main fact which emerges is that, when a person who has been blind since birth acquires the power of seeing things, as the result of an operation such as the removal of a cataract, he cannot interpret what he sees until he has undergone a prolonged period of training. The perception of visual ideas must be painstakingly learned, even by those who have had every opportunity during many years of learning about the world through the sense of touch. The main point on which von Senden differs from Mr Molineux is that he does not believe that the congenitally blind can fully distinguish between a cube and a sphere —even by touch. There is now no doubt that, whatever knowledge they may have had before, they do not see the difference between cube and sphere until they have been taught to do so.

The *gestalt* school of psychology has independently developed a philosophy which is essentially the same as that of Locke, but uses a different terminology. In the language of Locke, perception transforms sensations into ideas. In the language of Köhler (1930) meaning transforms sensations into things (or gestalten). There is no real difference between these statements, though the word *gestalt* is only applied to rather elaborate ideas. These psychologists have added much to our knowledge of perception; they have studied the ways in which significant ideas are selected from a mass of irrelevant sensations. They have shown that the meaning of a sensation commonly depends on the contrast between it and another sensation, or its position in a pattern of other sensations.

Locke's views on human understanding are widely accepted by scientists today. The existence of a real material world is a very likely hypothesis, though we can never be absolutely certain about it, since the words "absolutely certain" have no meaning, just as the words "irresistible force" have no meaning. Our ideas about the real world are constantly being modified in the light of experience, but essentially they are guesses and their value depends on their likelihood (Fisher, 1959). Locke's views were rejected by philosophers who wished to discover something about which they could be absolutely certain, not realizing that this was impossible.

Even when objects are observed directly their existence is not absolutely certain, though its likelihood may be very great. When we see a table we perceive a solid object with certain well defined properties. This perception serves a useful purpose by its effect on our behaviour and its value is not diminished by the fact that the physicist tells us that the space occupied by the table is only partly filled by molecules at great distances from one another, or by the fact that the physiologist tells us that our information is based on the interpretation of the meaning of electrical impulses in nerves.

It may seem strange to use the word idea in discussing the reactions of simple animals, but even simple brains must classify sensations in the same sort of way. One simple kind of perception occurs when a sensation is classified either as a sight or as a sound. The idea of a sight depends on previous experience of impulses arriving from the eye, and the idea of a sound depends on previous experience of impulses arriving from the ear. Quite simple brains can, however, analyse their perceptions in considerable detail, and in complex brains this must involve an elaborate mechanism. A recent book contains a fascinating account of the many senses of men and other animals (Milne and Milne, 1963).

A square piece of card may be perceived as a square piece of card, even though the image which it causes on the retina is seldom square and may vary widely in size and position. This problem has been widely discussed by psychologists (Hebb, 1949). Rosenblatt (1962) has constructed an apparatus, known as a perceptron, which can learn to perceive shapes. One model, for example, has a square retina consisting of 400 photo cells and can learn to distinguish the letters E and F in all possible positions and sizes.

The visual perception of shapes by cats has been analysed in some detail. The retina contains two types of ganglion cell—those with "on" receptive fields, which respond to an increase of light, and those with "off" receptive fields, which respond to a decrease of light. These cells send axons to the lateral geniculate body, which also contains "on" centres and "off" centres. These cells are sensitive to contrasting lights rather than to uniform illumination. Axons from the lateral geniculate body run to the visual cortex in the occipital lobe, which contains a number of functionally different types of cell. In one type the visual field is reproduced from point to point. Another type is sensitive to shapes of various kinds, such as long, narrow rectangles of light or darkness, or the borders between areas of different brightness running in a particular direction. In another type, the response is more complex and it is evident that such cells are part of the mechanism for perceiving shapes (Hubel and Wiesel, 1962) or the visual analyser (Pavlov, 1927).

Such processes provide a consistent picture of the outside world which can be tested by experiment and confirmed by the observations of other people. Some philosophers believed that they could discover what goes on inside the brain by direct observation of their own brains, using the method known as introspection. This led to much argument because the results varied widely from one philosopher to another and there was no way of deciding between them. J. B. Watson drew attention to the dangers of this kind of argument, when he founded the behaviourist school of psychology, which studies behaviour and rejects introspection. He saved the world from a great deal of idle argument about facts, but the attempt to avoid all ideas derived from introspection has led to arguments of another kind. The theory, discussed above, that perception transforms sensations into ideas was originally based on introspection, but some such process must occur whenever an animal gives an intelligent response. The ideas of fear, hunger, pain and rage were based on introspection, but Cannon (1915) wrote a book about their bodily effects and showed that they described changes which did occur. According to one school of thought, it is unscientific to speak as if a rat could feel the emotion of fear, since we have no direct knowledge of what the rat feels. On the other hand, we also lack direct knowledge of the feelings of other human beings and our knowledge of our own feelings is suspect because it is due to introspection. Rats and men both react to danger by giving responses which are classified as fear. These include such symptoms as trembling and avoidance and it is a reasonable hypothesis that similar mechanisms are involved in both cases and thus reasonable to use the word fear to describe responses of this type (Miller, 1964). The response may vary widely according to the individual and according to the situation, and it would be most unfortunate if the use of the word fear obscured these variations. On the other hand, the actions of certain drugs have been explained on the theory that they diminish fear. This explanation is not necessarily unscientific (Steinberg, 1964). Similar arguments apply to the theory that rats give the response appropriate to hunger, pain and rage. It is convenient, for the sake of brevity, to say that the rats may feel these emotions and the evidence that they do feel them is as good as the evidence that human beings feel them, although the emotions of a rat appear to be less complex than those which would be felt by a human being in the same circumstances.

On the other hand, ideas derived entirely from introspection unsupported by objective observations, may be misleading. For example, there has been much argument about the idea expressed by the word "mind". The workings of the brain are most easily understood on the theory that this idea has no relation at all to anything real. The world has come to believe in it because there has been much talk about it and because there is a convenient name for it, but this does not prove that it exists. Experiments based on extrasensory perception have suggested that mind may exist independently of brain, but experiments are difficult and very little is known of its properties (Gaddum, 1956).

Ideas are of two kinds:

1. *Objective ideas*—such as hand, white, electron, etc. If the above argument is accepted, fear should be classified as an objective idea. These ideas are based on sensations and may be studied by experiments which can be confirmed by others.

2. *Subjective ideas*—such as mind and free-will, and the material of which logic and mathematics, poetry and religion are made. These are based on introspection and cannot be studied experimentally.They are dependent on language and would represent nothing at all if no word had been invented to express them. They presumably play no part in the behaviour of other animals, but they are important for man because his social life has become dependent on them. When he is young a man learns to believe that each man has a mind capable of exerting free-will, and he learns what can be done by manipulating words and numbers. Civilization, with its rewards and punishments, is based on these ideas, but they are beyond the scope of the present discussion.

III. Learning

The work of Pavlov and his pupils will not be discussed in detail here. It provides a mass of information about the physiology of the cerebral cortex, which is generally recognized to be of the greatest importance. When some of the simpler facts have been explained in neurophysiological and biochemical terms, it may be possible to explain some of the more complicated phenomena.

Pavlov's original experiments depended on the measurement and timing of salivary secretion. This response had the advantages that it could be measured in a conscious dog and yet appeared to be independent of voluntary control. In these experiments the conditioned stimulus (a bell or a light, originally inadequate to elicit salivation) was repeatedly followed by food (the unconditioned stimulus). Eventually the conditioned stimulus caused salivation even when there was no food. This technique was used to analyse the dog's sensations and its powers of sensory discrimination. In these early experiments there was little scope for changes in the motor response. It was found essential that the conditioned stimulus (CS or signal) preceded the unconditioned stimulus (US) in time.

An American school of psychologists has used a different technique to produce "operant" conditioning (Skinner, 1938), or "instrumental learning" (Miller, 1961). In these experiments the animal either learns for itself by trial and error, or is taught, that something which it does leads to pleasant results, or avoids unpleasant results. It may, for example, learn that pressing a lever produces food, or that moving to another part of its cage saves it from electric shocks. Once this initial lesson has been learnt, the animal can be taught to give the appropriate response to some sensations and not others, and its powers of discrimination may be tested; in addition, it is possible to follow the extent to which the motor response can be adjusted. This is a simple example of an acquired skill.

Russian work on conditioned reflexes was briefly summarized and criticized by Konorski (1948) in a book dedicated to I. P. Pavlov and C. S. Sherrington, in which he hoped to do something to bridge the gulf between their respective achievements. Konorski points out that Pavlov's concepts are sometimes vague and that he did not always use words in their conventional sense. When, for example, he spoke of the irradiation of inhibition over the cortex, he did not mean that the cells were themselves inhibited, but that the effects of a reflex inhibiting salivation (for example) was spreading, and the evidence for this was indirect.

Pavlov's interpretation of his results was also criticized by Hebb (1949) from the point of view of the psychologists. One important fact is that the appearance of food leads not only to salivation, but also to eating movements. When the dog hears the bell he salivates, but he does not usually make eating movements, with his nose in the food dish. According to Pavlov's original theory, it is supposed that the conditioned stimulus makes connexions with the whole motor response to the unconditioned stimulus. The brain appears to be able to select some parts of the response in a purposeful sort of way.

Learning is thought to be governed by the "law of effect", which says, roughly speaking, that an act which is closely followed by satisfaction, pleasure or comfort will be learnt, while one which is followed by discomfort will be eliminated. The matter is not quite so simple, since mild punishment may, in some cases, increase learning, but it is agreed that there must be some mechanism in the brain which decides what will be learnt. Perhaps this difficulty can be avoided by calling anything which leads to learning a reward, and anything which has the opposite effect a punishment or negative reward. A reward leads to a positive conditioned reflex, and a punishment leads to a negative conditioned reflex and avoidance. According to Hull (1951), a reward is essentially something which leads to a reduction of drive; this attractive generalization has led to much controversy. There is some evidence that the intellectual satisfaction that comes from the perception of relations between ideas may itself be a reward.

The two types of conditioning are called Type I and Type II (Konorski, 1948). Type I conditioning is classical Pavlovian conditioning, typified by experiments with salivation. Type II conditioning is essentially the same as operant conditioning. The main characteristics of Type II conditioning are:

1. It depends on recording the movements of voluntary muscle.
2. It appears to involve purpose. The animal makes the movement in

order to produce the desired result. Pavlov felt that some theory was necessary to explain purpose, but most writers accept drive as an objective fact, and drive implies purpose.

3. It depends in the first place on trial and error. Under the influence of some drive, the animals make movements which may be random, but often appear to be intelligent. It may, for example, be driven by hunger to seek food or it may be driven by fear to avoid pain. Sometimes an animal will learn without any obvious material reward. This type of learning has been called latent learning, or it may be said that the animal is driven by curiosity to seek knowledge.

The drive may sometimes depend on the fact that a conditioned stimulus has been applied and no reward has been received. When the movements of the animal lead to a reward, a reflex is formed which has the effect that the CS, or the drive, leads to the appropriate movements. Much of the work that has been done on operant conditioning has been devoted to the study of the ways in which the animal adapts its behaviour in the light of experience. The technique makes it possible to study the motor side of conditioned reflexes. In Pavlov's experiments on salivation, the response chosen varied quantitatively but not qualitatively, and this excluded the study of changes in the motor response.

In these experiments on salivation, where the presence of food is the unconditioned stimulus, there is no obvious material reward for salivation. The same is true of the interoceptive reflexes reviewed by Razran (1961), where the CS, the US, or both, are delivered to the mucous membrane of some internal organ. As in the case of latent learning discussed above, the fact that the reward is not obvious does not prove that there is no reward. In the case of salivation, the reward may be the satisfaction that is derived from the proper digestion of food.

It has been suggested that rewards in general may be connected with the mechanism discovered by Olds and Milner (Olds, 1962; see also Stein, 1964). They implanted electrodes in the brains of rats and then allowed the rats to stimulate their own brains by pressing on a lever. When the electrodes are in certain parts of the brain, the rats press the lever more than once a second for hours on end, neglecting food and sleep for the purpose. Other areas of brain are much less effective, 60% of the brain is neutral and a small area gives negative results, the animals touching the lever once and then avoiding it. Similar results have since been obtained with monkeys, cats and other animals. The positive rewarding area is centred on the posterior hypothalamus and includes most of the rhinencephalon and parts of the thalamus and basal ganglia. The small negative area is in the dorsal and lateral hypothalamus and extends into the mid-brain. It seems likely that when a pattern in the cortex leads to stimulation of the positive rewarding area, positive feedback will occur, and the pattern will be repeated, and that this will lead to the formation of conditioned reflexes. However, experiments with bees show that elaborate mechanisms are unnecessary for simple learning.

In discussing the formation of conditioned reflexes, it must be remembered that the conditioned stimulus (CS) must come before the unconditioned stimulus (US).

Doty (1961) quotes various examples of facilitation between the responses of a single unit to two different nerves in various parts of the body, where the first stimulus may increase the effect of a second stimulus applied a few milliseconds later. He says that the time sequence is different from that which occurs in a conditioned reflex, where the first stimulus (CS) has no effect on the response to a second stimulus (US), and calls this the temporal paradox of conditioning. This argument is difficult to understand, since the effect of the first stimulus (CS) in a conditioned reflex is to reduce the threshold for the second stimulus (US) to zero; the time sequence is the same in the two cases.

Another temporal paradox occurs in experiments on trial and error and operant conditioning—when the response occurs before the reward. This requires some explanation since causes are generally followed by effects, but in this case the cause—the reward—appears to follow the effect—the response (Stein, 1964). It may be said that the cause is not the reward itself but the expectation of reward, but it is then necessary to consider what is meant by expectation, and this is important since it is at the basis of all purposeful movements. As stated above, Pavlov felt that purpose should be explained but other writers accept it as an objective fact.

When a new conditioned reflex is formed, there is a pattern in the plastic nerve net, partly caused by the CS, partly resulting from the motor response elicited by the US. The unconditioned reflex does not necessarily involve high centres at all and information about it presumably reaches the plastic nerve net through proprioceptive nerves. For example, information about the movements of muscles reaches the somæsthetic area of the cortex from spindles in the muscle and from sensory receptors in joints and tendons, through the medial lemniscus or the spinothalamic tract. Information also arrives through the various centres controlling posture. The formation of a conditioned reflex involving muscular movement, depends on interaction between these proprioceptive impulses and the pattern which is already present in the plastic nerve net. Something rather like this is shown in a diagram by Eccles (1953).

At some points in the nerve net, both CS and US will increase activity and new channels will be opened. At others, both will cause partial inhibition and new areas of complete inhibition will be formed. If some process makes these changes persist, the pattern corresponding to the CS eventually has so much in common with the pattern corresponding to the US that it causes the appropriate motor response. This process is discussed below in the section dealing with mechanisms.

The connexion between the proprioceptive nerves and the response is probably strengthened by positive feedback, the discovery of which is one of the most exciting advances in modern physiology. There are special motor nerves which increase the sensitivity of the peripheral sensory organs such as the eye and the ear and the muscle spindles and their central pathways (Livingston, 1959).

When the interval between the CS and the US is increased, response is delayed. During the interval the patterns in the cortex are presumably evolving in a more or less standard way (as discussed below) until the pattern is that which originally interacted with the proprioceptive impulses arising from the US. This leads to association between the motor response to the US and one particular pattern in the series, so that a delayed reflex is formed. Pavlov called this a trace reflex.

When the US comes before the CS, there is no particular reason why the CS should ever lead to the pattern effected by both stimuli since patterns evolve in one direction only, and that is why no conditioned reflex is formed. In order to form a reflex, the CS must come before the US, or, at any rate, the CS must start before the US ends.

When the US does not occur with sufficient regularity to form either a positive or a negative conditioned reflex, no reflex is formed and any responses occurring during this period tend to be suppressed. This is what Pavlov called internal inhibition and what is sometimes called habituation (Thorpe, 1963). It must be a very important mechanism since it prevents the plastic nerve net from being distracted by unimportant problems. Pavlov showed that animals sometimes had remarkable powers of discriminating between those sights and sounds which led to conditioned reflexes and other similar sights and sounds which led to internal inhibition.

In order to obtain regular results, it is often necessary that the US should be repeated many times, but it is possible for an association to be formed as the result of a single experience. In this case, the association is presumably such that it causes the same series of patterns to be evolved repeatedly in the nerve net, so that they become fixed, or that several different series of patterns all lead back to the same original pattern. This must depend on the previous experience of the animal.

Pavlov showed that if a stimulus A formed a conditioned reflex with an unconditioned stimulus B, then B might in its turn act as CS for an unconditioned stimulus C forming a secondary reflex, so that the conditioned stimulus A would lead to the response C. Such mechanisms tend to simplify themselves since the stimulus A is regularly followed by the unconditioned stimulus C and must tend to form a direct association with it. When a response has been learned, the way it was learned may be forgotten.

Figure 1 shows the nervous pathways which might be involved in the simplified situation where a classical Pavlovian (Type I) conditioned reflex has been formed involving one kind of response. The proprioceptive impulses recording the response interact with the patterns formed by the CS to form the reflex.

If CS_1 is regularly followed by US which leads to a response R, which is associated with a reward, then a conditioned reflex will be formed. If CS_2 is not regularly followed by US then the animal learns to distinguish between CS_1 and CS_2 so that CS_1 causes a response and CS_2

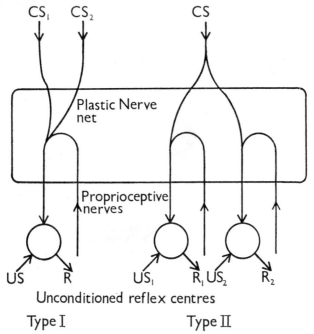

Fig. 1.

causes internal inhibition. This mechanism was used by Pavlov and others to test an animal's powers of sensory discrimination.

Operant or Type II conditioning makes it possible to study the motor side of the reflex. If R_1 is a reward and R_2 is not, nervous pathways leading to R_1 will be facilitated and those leading to R_2 will not. This is an example of trial and error in its simplest form. The animal tries two responses, adopts one and rejects the other.

In more natural conditions the situation is likely to be more complex. There are likely to be a number of responses R_1, R_2, R_3, etc. differing very little from one another and forming a continuous series, with some overlapping of effects so that the unconditioned stimulus US_{10}, for example, causes not only the typical response R_{10} but also other similar responses such as R_8, R_9, R_{11} and R_{12}. If one of these responses is rewarded and the others are not then the appropriate reflex will be formed. In this way the motor response which earns most rewards will become the basis of a conditioned reflex. The behaviour of the animal becomes adapted to its needs.

When the reflex is first formed the response may involve a variety of movements. Those which are invariably associated with a reward are reinforced and those which are associated with no reward, or a negative reward, are eliminated so that the total response becomes simpler and more automatic and the animal has acquired a skill.

When none of the immediate movements R_1, R_2, etc. leads to a reward the animal may eventually solve the problem by reasoning. This may depend on the manipulation of ideas until a combination is found which leads to a reward. This must involve much trial and error, but some of the best brains can arrive at a solution without actually making all the movements involved. This kind of trial and error may be very rapid, so that the animal appears to have immediate insight of the solution.

The behaviour of chimpanzees in new situations, where direct methods of earning rewards have failed, was studied by Köhler (1925). When a banana lies outside the cage and cannot be reached by hand the ape may use a stick to bring it nearer, and in one famous case an ape found by accident that two short sticks could be fitted together to make a longer stick, and then immediately realized that this longer stick would enable it to rake in a banana which had previously been too far away. Köhler was impressed with the fact that such problems were not solved by ordinary trial and error, but by some much more effective process in the brain, but his observations do not disprove the theory that this process consisted in something analogous to trial and error among ideas.

IV. Instincts

Complex behaviour which is not based on learning, or on intelligence, is called instinctive. The word instinct has been used in many different ways and it is difficult, but unnecessary, to define it precisely. The reproductive instinct causes birds to make love, build nests, lay eggs, incubate them and raise families. The possession of ovaries and hormones is a necessary condition for the laying of eggs, but it is equally essential that an instinct causes the eggs to be laid in the nest and incubated.

A simple instinct is the same thing as a complex unconditioned reflex. When a painful stimulus is applied to a limb, the limb is withdrawn. This movement is commonly regarded as a reflex, but might be regarded as a simple instinct to avoid pain. On the other hand, the word instinct is sometimes used to include whole groups of reflexes. McDougall (see Tinbergen, 1951) listed 12 instincts—fear, repulsion, pugnacity, curiosity, self abasement, self assertion, parental, reproduction, gregariousness, emulation, acquisitiveness and hunger—others have listed many more. Scott (1962) lists the following patterns of behaviour—ingestive, eliminative, sexual, care-giving, care-soliciting, agonistic (fight and flight), imitative, shelter-seeking and investigative. According to Tinbergen (1951) instincts can be classified into a graded series. For example, the reproductive instinct of the male stickleback includes instincts for fighting, building, mating and care of offspring; the fighting instinct includes instincts for chasing, biting, threatening, etc. The simplest responses, such as biting and chasing are called consummatory acts; they occur at the end of a bout of activity and their performance acts as a reward and diminishes the drive which comes mainly from the more complex instincts such as the fighting instinct. Some of these more complex instincts depend on centres in the hypothalamus, stimulation of which may cause rage, hunger or thirst and cause the animal to make the movements associated with fighting and seeking for food and drink. Many of these responses are inherited and automatic; but they are commonly purposeful and may be modified by the experience of the individuals so that their purpose is more likely to be achieved. Hunger leads to the movements associated with the search for food, which may at first appear like random trial and error, but which soon become conditioned by the mechanisms discussed above so that the animal behaves intelligently.

The release of an instinct may depend upon various factors:

1. Electrical stimulation of certain areas of the hypothalamus through implanted electrodes makes animals eat, and stimulation of other areas makes them starve. Extirpation of these areas has the opposite effects so that operated animals may become grossly fat or miserably thin (Hess, 1957; Brobeck, 1960; Miller, 1960).

2. Administration of drugs or hormones. Sexual behaviour is increased by sex hormones and there is evidence that this may be due to a direct action of the hormone on the brain. For example, Harris, Michael and Scott (1958) implanted small amounts of stilbœstrol dibutyrate in the posterior hypothalamus of female cats whose ovaries had been removed. This led to the development of sexual behaviour lasting more than two months, but larger doses of the hormone implanted elsewhere had no such effect. Grossman (1960) implanted crystals of drugs into an area of the hypothalamus of rats through a needle and found that adrenaline or noradrenaline caused the rats to eat, while acetylcholine or carbachol, implanted through the same needle, caused them to drink.

3. The perception of complex ideas which become associated with the "Innate Releasing Mechanism" (Tinbergen, 1951). This association

may occur slowly, and be gradually conditioned by the experience of the individual, or it may occur with surprising speed. There is an instinct which makes certain kinds of young birds follow their parents, but it does not tell them what their parents look like. If a human being is present during the first few hours of the bird's life the bird may become attached to him and follow him about and treat him as if he were the real parent. This process is known as imprinting; the critical period during which it occurs may not last more than a few hours and after that it is almost irreversible (Lorenz, 1952).

The rate at which a learned response becomes a motor habit varies widely in different species of animal. Lorenz (1952) describes some interesting observations on water shrews. These small mammals belong to the order Insectivora and are thus very distantly related to the rodents and carnivores and primates which have been more widely studied. These particular animals are nearly blind and depend on the sense of touch for their knowledge of the world. They feel their way about with sensitive and actively mobile whiskers. This is at first a slow process, but when they have been the same way several times before, they cover the ground more quickly by repeating the same movements at a much greater speed. When a shrew has acquired a motor habit in this way it follows it as strictly as a railway engine follows its tracks. In one experiment this involved jumping on and off two stones which lay in their path and when the stones were moved the shrews still jumped in the air at the point where the stones had been. They came down with a jarring bump and were obviously disconcerted, but they went back and tried again and crashed down exactly as they had before. It was only then that they realized that their path had been altered and that they must learn their way again by the slow method involving touch. So long as everything remains the same, this ability to form motor habits compensates the shrews for being nearly blind and allows them to run fast. An animal such as a mouse has better vision, and would not try to jump on a stone that was not there.

V. Patterns in the Cortex

The theory to be considered now is that the patterns of activity in the cerebral cortex are constantly evolving, so that successive patterns are related to one another like the individual pictures on a cinematograph film. This evolution is partly intrinsic and inevitable in the sense that any given pattern is likely to be followed by the same series of patterns, but the series is interrupted and modified by the arrival of sensory impulses.

The theory that the activity of the central nervous system depends on constantly changing patterns is an old one. Lashley (1929) came to the conclusion that "the activity of the visual cortex must resemble that of one of the electric signs in which a pattern of letters passes rapidly across a stationary group of lamps." He probably did not mean this analogy to be taken too literally. He wanted to emphasize that it was the pattern of activity which mattered and not the individual cells.

Sherrington (1946) compared the brain with an "enchanted loom where millions of flashing shuttles weave a dissolving pattern, always a meaningful pattern though never an abiding one". Grey Walter (1953) showed this pattern vividly in his toposcope, in which each of a number of flashing lights is connected with a different spot on the brain, so that the observer sees "a sparkling field of rhythmic flashing points with trains of travelling sparks hurrying hither and thither". Gestalt psychologists (Köhler, 1930) speak of a state of developing dynamical distribution, which is presumably the same thing seen from another point of view.

The human cortex has been estimated to contain about 10^{10} cells. In a given small interval of time each cell either responds or does not. The total number of patterns possible is, therefore, about $[2^{10}]^{10}$ or 10^{30}. This is a very large number compared with the number of milliseconds in 70 years (2×10^{12}), so that if there were no other limiting factors it would easily be possible for an individual to have a different pattern in his cerebral cortex every millisecond of his life.

It is reasonable to suppose this pattern to be related to sub-conscious thoughts in the mind of the animal, which tend to succeed one another in a repeatable way, but may develop along new and original lines. These thoughts may have no obvious logical connexion with one another. On the other hand, they may be associated with motor activity and acquired skills and so be related more directly to the outside world. The proprioceptive response to each movement becomes the conditioned stimulus for the next movement. This occurs when a child learns to recite poetry or a musician learns to play an instrument. Eventually the acquired skill becomes automatic—the nervous pathways are shortened and simpler proprioceptive reflexes are formed.

The automatic development of patterns implies that the brain can repeat the same patterns and the same thoughts over and over again and provides a mechanism for one of the stages of memory discussed below.

When the brain is in a relaxed state, or during light sleep, the cortex gives electrical oscillations with a frequency of 8–12/sec., known as the alpha-rhythm. Any sudden stimulation causes this to be replaced by more frequent activity of lower voltage which forms part of the orienting response. Adrian and Matthews (1934) suggested that, during the alpha rhythm, groups of cells were active together and that the response to stimuli was due to desynchronization. This can be recorded electrophysiologically with implanted electrodes in the cerebral cortex of conscious animals (Morrell, 1961). If the signal is visual, acoustic or proprioceptive, desynchronization may occur in the appropriate area of cortex and if the stimulus is strong enough it spreads over the whole cortex. Rheinberger and Jasper (1937), coined the term "activation pattern" to describe this response. One factor controlling the spread of patterns is clearly the strength of the stimulus.

The spread of any given pattern presumably also depends on its relation to the pattern already present. If these two patterns are similar, they are likely to reinforce one another, but, if they are not, it is likely that the new pattern will have little effect. In psychological language the animal will be more affected by the new signal if it is already thinking about it and directing its attention to it.

Attention in mammals is a complex process. When a strange object appears the animal gives the orienting response. It concentrates its eyes and ears and its other sense organs upon it and these become more sensitive owing to the action of special motor nerves (Livingston, 1959). On the other hand, attention may be aroused in quite small nerve nets, since the attention of a moth may be directed towards a particular source of light or smell. Attention commonly occupies the whole mind, though some gifted human beings can pay attention to more than one thing at a time. Attention to any one object presumably corresponds to one particular pattern in the nerve net. When the brain is attending to one particular object, the nerve net is adjusted so that it is only affected by sensations which may be related to the object of interest, while other sensations are neglected and their effects inhibited.

Attention is due to the formation of a new pattern in the cerebrum. This may occur in at least two ways:

1. It may be due to sensory impulses reaching the cerebrum through the well-known specific projection system with a more or less point-to-point arrangement. Sensations from the eye, ear or body cause arousal by imposing the appropriate pattern on the cerebrum in this way.

2. It may be due to impulses in ascending fibres from the reticular formation, much of which lies near the mid-line and in the mid-brain. It is sometimes supposed that these fibres cause unspecific arousal, and this may be true when they are stimulated electrically, but it is probable that their normal function is to lay down a precise pattern of activity in the cerebrum, so that the attention of the brain is directed to thoughts which are dictated by them. This mechanism is likely to be active whether the animal is awake or asleep. The reticular formation provides a mechanism by which the attention of the brain is directed into new channels.

The spread of activity through the cortex may be studied by following the immediate effects of electrical stimulation. In the intact cortex of anæsthetized rabbits this depends on facilitation and is only shown in response to a series of stimuli, which starts waves which travel 5–8 mm. (Adrian, 1936). Burns (1958) has studied the transmission of impulses in isolated slabs of cat's cortex measuring about 20 × 5 mm. These slabs do not have the "spontaneous" activity which makes such experiments difficult in intact cortex, and Burns was able to study the spread of impulses in some detail. When such slabs of isolated cortex are stimulated electrically, there is a surface negative response which spreads about 10 mm., is independent of anæsthesia, and probably does not involve synapses. This response is thought to depend on all the fibres which happen to be near the electrode and is unlikely to be important from the functional point of view.

Stronger stimuli cause a surface positive response, which is thought to be due to a negative change in a layer of cells (B cells) about 1 mm. below the surface. These cells are at about the same depth as the acetylcholine-sensitive cells studied by Krnjević and Phillis (1962); they may perhaps be the same cells. The surface positive response is sensitive to anæsthetics and in the unanæsthetized animal a single shock causes a prolonged response which spreads without attenuation in all directions to the borders of the isolated area. The discharge may last 0·5–5 seconds. Burns considers that such bursts of activity might be due to self re-excitation by impulses passing round a closed circuit, to persistent chemical transmitters, or to differential re-polarization, in which one part of a neuron becomes re-polarized before the other parts of the neuron and is then re-stimulated by them. It is clear, in any case, that this response must have some important function. Its possible relation to immediate memory is discussed below.

The study of the spread of the effects of electrical stimuli over wider areas of the cortex is more difficult owing to "spontaneous activity", but Burns and Smith (1962) have inserted microelectrodes in the cortex of unanæsthetized cats and analysed the results statistically. They came to the conclusion that a response to local excitation could be demonstrated all over the accessible cortex.

There is some evidence to suggest that a pattern of activity may spread from one centre, so that it may eventually organize the whole nerve net. This is illustrated by the experiments of Myers (1956) and Sperry (1956), who divided the optic chiasma of cats and rats in the mid-line, so that the right eye was connected with the right optical cortex only and the left eye with the left cortex only. One eye was then blindfolded and the animal was trained to respond predictably to visual stimuli. The other eye was then blindfolded instead, and it was found that the animal gave correct responses to stimuli applied to the eye and the cortex which had not been trained. The pattern must have spread from one side of the cortex to the other, through the corpus callosum. This was shown by the fact that there was no transfer of information when the corpus callosum had been completely divided. When a bridge of corpus callosum only 2 mm. wide was left intact, information was transferred. This result reveals a mechanism which is likely to be fundamental in the study of behaviour. A fuller account of this work is given by Wooldridge (1963).

A similar transfer of patterns was shown in the experiments of Burns (see Ochs, 1962). Spreading depression was caused on one side by the application of 25% KCl to the surface of the cortex of rats. This has the effect of temporary decortication. Food-conditioned reflexes, and avoidance-conditioned reflexes, were then established in the cortex on the other side. This trained side was then depressed and it was shown that the side which had originally been depressed had learned nothing, but when the reflex was elicited ten times, without depression of either side and without reward, information was transferred from one side to the other. This was shown by the fact that the rat learned, with unexpected rapidity, to give the appropriate response when the side which had originally been trained was depressed.

VI. Mechanisms

The factors controlling the spread of impulses through a nerve net were discussed by Beurle (1957). His model is simple compared with what must occur in living brains and in the following account it has been simplified still further and numerical values for some of the unknown quantities have been inserted.

A nerve cell (neuron) is stimulated by impulses arriving at synapses on the dendrites. Each impulse causes a local excitation, presumably involving partial depolarization of the dendritic membrane, which would be recorded as a postsynaptic potential. When the total excitation in a cell rises to a threshold value, there is a short delay known as the operating period (T, 0·5 msec.) after which the cells become active, and an all-or-none impulse passes down the axon. In the simplest case, it is assumed that this happens when q (10) impulses arrive within a definite period (4 msec.). There is then a refractory period r (10–100 msec.) during which the arrival of impulses has no effect; these refractory cells are said to be "used".

The branches of each neuron act on a large number of synapses in other cells. An expression is obtained for the rate at which the concentration of these cells falls off with their distance (x) from the original cell. The activity at any given place (x) and time (t) is measured by F, which is equal to the proportion of cells becoming active per unit time. The rate at which impulses arrive at secondary cells depends on the total activity in the neighbourhood and is calculated by integrating a function of F with respect to both x and t.

It can be calculated that waves of activity would pass through such a mass of cells, leaving used cells behind them. The size of a wave is measured by M, which is equal to the proportion of all the cells used during its passage. At one critical value of M (M_0) the size of the wave will remain constant, but if M is greater than this it will increase until all the cells are used, and if it is less than M_0 it will decrease until the wave disappears. The system is thus unstable, unless it is controlled in some way. The important question for such models is how the size of the waves is controlled. Beurle suggested that there are two special kinds of nerve fibres, E and I. In his theory the E-fibres increase the size of waves by subthreshold stimulation and the I-fibres produce the opposite effect by causing actual discharges of cells and so increasing the number of "used" cells. The E-fibres would be active when the result was a reward, and the I-fibres when it was a punishment, so that E-fibres would lead to conditioned reflexes and I-fibres would lead to inhibition. Such a mechanism is possible, but there are other possibilities.

In Beurle's model a localized sensory stimulus first causes effects in a region where wave size increases and spreads over a wider area. The activity then passes through a middle region where wave size is modified by the experience of the animal and then through another region where wave size decreases and is restricted to a smaller area, so that eventually only a small group of motor cells are activated. The actual position of these cells and the movement produced may be expected to depend on the fine structure of the wave.

Three special mechanisms are supposed to operate in the middle area to account for conditioned reflexes, purpose and reasoning:

1. The passage of impulses causes facilitation, so that the passage of other impulses over the same part becomes easier. When the same two waves frequently cross the mass of cells simultaneously, those features which are common to both are facilitated, so that eventually both have the same effect and lead to the same motor response. This is the basis of conditioned reflexes.

2. When the motor response leads to a desirable result the pattern of activity is reinforced. When it leads to an undesirable result, the pattern of activity is suppressed. This facilitates patterns which lead to desirable results and suppresses patterns which lead to undesirable results and is the basis of purpose.

3. In some cases when the motor response is inhibited the pattern of the wave is carried back to the sensory side of the mass of cells and fed into it again. The process is repeated until it produces a desirable result, which then leads to action. This is the basis of reasoning.

Beurle's theory has been welcomed by some physiologists (Gerard, 1960). It may perhaps serve as a basis for discussion, but more recent work suggests various modifications. In the form given here it is undoubtedly too simple. It takes no account of the chemical theory of transmission at nerve endings or of inhibition, both of which are discussed below. It provides no direct theory of attention, or of the way the brain can recapitulate the past, which have already been discussed.

When the attention of a resting brain is aroused the alpha rhythm disappears. It is reasonable to suppose that this change involves the inhibition of some mechanism which transmits impulses from one cell to another of the same bundle, so that they all respond together. According to Magnes, Moruzzi and Pompeiano (1961) these synchronizing structures are in the lower brain stem.

There are presumably many ways in which patterns of activity may develop but one possibility is that the pattern depends on islands of blocked cells between which the waves of activity pass. In some places a wave will pass an island on each side and meet itself again at one particular place to be reinforced. The passage of waves will depend on the whole pattern of waves in all the channels. Some waves will be reinforced by the simultaneous arrival of other waves through other channels. Others will be suppressed because the tissues are insensitive after the passage of a wave. Such a mechanism should be very selective, in the sense that a signal consisting of impulses of a given pattern in space and time would pass through, while other signals would be suppressed. This selectivity would depend on the shape and arrangement of the islands of blocked cells. If this theory is correct, the meaning of the pattern depends not only on the spatial distribution of the waves but also on their time relations.

The pattern must be constantly changing, but the islands of block may be expected to introduce some degree of stability, so that successive patterns are all concerned with different aspects of the same subject. Within this framework the same or a similar series of patterns is likely to be repeated. On the other hand, the pattern must undergo comparatively slow changes caused by the impulses which pass through.

According to this theory, desynchronization and the disappearance of alpha waves are due to inhibition, which is suddenly imposed when the animal wakes up, and gradually increases and develops while it is awake. It may be suggested that during the day the inhibition spreads and eventually becomes excessive, so that the brain becomes less efficient and eventually goes to sleep. During sleep the inhibition disappears and the brain recovers. This naïve theory explains why sleep is necessary, but it is not immediately obvious how it is related to all the other facts that are known about sleep. The apparent occurrence of inhibition during arousal has, however, been discussed by Bremer (1961).

Chemical transmission   There is evidence that some neurons in the brain act by liberating chemical substances at their endings. When such a chemical transmitter acts on the dendrites it has a local effect, increasing or decreasing the polarization of the membrane. Eccles (1953) has studied the responses of motoneurons in the spinal cord and concludes that the initiation of an impulse in the axon depends on the sum of the electric effects of all the synapses. When this depolarization reaches a threshold value in the initial segment of the axon, the membrane on its surface becomes very permeable first to sodium and then to potassium ions. Sodium ions flow into the axon and the electric current due to this flow stimulates another segment of axon so that an electric impulse passes down the axon. This is essentially the type of cell which formed the basis of Beurle's theory.

There is good evidence that some neurons in the central nervous system act by liberating acetylcholine; and the distribution of these nerves (cholinergic neurons) can be determined by studying in different parts of the brain the distribution of acetylcholine itself and the enzyme choline-acetylase which forms it. These neurons account for a comparatively small proportion of the brain and it seems likely that other neurons liberate other substances, but we do not know what these other substances are. Extracts contain a large number of other pharmacologically active substances including various amines, amino acids, polypeptides, lipids and unsaturated fats, and it is probable that some of these act as chemical transmitters though the evidence for this is incomplete. In any case it is possible that some neurons liberate substances which have not yet been discovered. The substances liberated by inhibitor cells such as the Renshaw cells, the pyramidal tracts, the first sensory neuron in the spinal cord and the optic nerve have not been identified (Gaddum, 1963).

Experiments on chemical transmission at peripheral synapses have shown that drugs may affect transmission in many different ways and it is possible that the body releases substances having some of these effects. It is, therefore, easy to suggest various ways in which the brain might be controlled. For example, drugs may cause the release of chemical transmitters or inhibit this release; they may preserve them from destruction or prevent their action; they may also act like local anæsthetics on axons, or produce effects by acting on the blood supply. Drugs may inhibit enzymes or cause their formation; the adaptive formation of enzymes is a slow process which might be responsible for prolonged changes in the brain.

There is no need to consider such theories at present, but it is important to discuss how many of the properties of plastic nerve nets, such as the cerebral cortex, can be accounted for in terms of the properties of transmission in the spinal cord and other simpler nerve nets. This subject has been reviewed by Eccles (1964).

Facilitation   The theory to be considered here, like most other theories of the mode of action of nerve nets, assumes that neuronal activity results in an irreversible change at a synapse. A series of impulses following one another quickly has more effect than a single impulse, a phenomenon called facilitation.

Summation of post-synaptic potentials occurs when the interval between stimuli is a few milliseconds. A small dose of the chemical transmitter causes some depolarization in the dendrites, without starting an impulse. This may be antagonized by inhibitory nerves which increase polarization. The combined effects of polarization and depolarization on the initial segment of the axon may start an impulse or a series of impulses. This theory provides a mechanism for the combined action of impulses in different axons acting on the same neuron, provided that they arrive within a few milliseconds of one another. This type of combination is likely to play a fundamental part in the integrative action of nervous systems, since it leads to impulses in new pathways. It is possible that there is only the one mechanism for this. Changes of longer duration may be secondary to this primary effect.

The phenomenon known as post-activation potentiation or post-tetanic potentiation (Hughes, 1958) is clearly different from that which has just been discussed. This term has been applied to phenomena occuring in a variety of neural junctions in the central and peripheral nervous systems, in which the response to a single stimulus is increased by applying a quick series of similar stimuli in the form of a tetanus. For example, Lloyd (1949) delivered a series of single shocks at intervals of 2·4 sec. to the nerve supplying the gastrocnemius of a cat and recorded the reflex response electrically from the first sacral root. The nerve was then stimulated at a rate of 555/sec. for 12 sec., after which the response to a single stimulus increased about 7 times, reaching a maximum in about 15 sec. and then falling to its original level in 3 minutes.

This post-activation potentiation differs from post-synaptic facilitation in the following ways:—

1. It lasts much longer. In some of the examples quoted by Hughes (1958), it lasted minutes or even hours.
2. It is pre-synaptic in origin.
3. Both the tetanus and the testing stimulus must be applied to the same neuron.

Post-activation potentiation also occurs when the effect is inhibitory. It thus increases both excitation and inhibition, and might be expected to make the system unstable. Most of the neurons in the brain of an animal are continuously active while the animal is awake, and any transient increase of frequency would be expected to cause potentiation and increased effects on other neurons, so that the response would be amplified. If several neurons were connected in a chain, the amplification would be large, unless it were controlled in some way (Fessard and Szabo, quoted by Delasfresnaye, 1961).

These experiments show that amplification may occur, but do not show how it occurs. The release of acetylcholine (Katz, 1958) and other transmitters (Dudel and Kuffler, 1961) is a quantal process. Acetylcholine is thought to be contained in synaptic vesicles which rupture slowly in a resting nerve, causing miniature post-synaptic potentials.

An impulse in the nerve increases the rate of release and, if several impulses follow at suitable intervals, the number of quanta liberated each time increases. There is evidence that a prolonged tetanus may cause hyperpolarization of the pre-synaptic nerve ending leading to a larger pre-synaptic spike potential and increased transmission through the synapse (Eccles, 1961b). This is presumably due to the increase in the number of quanta of transmitter released.

It has been suggested also that potentiation is due to the accumulation of the transmitter, or of potassium, or to impulses reverberating in closed circuits. It might also be due to differential re-polarization like that caused by veratrine in peripheral muscles; one part of the muscle recovers more quickly than other parts and is then re-stimulated by their action currents. The suggestion of Burns (1958) that a similar process may cause after-discharges in the cerebral cortex has already been discussed.

It has been suggested (Hebb, 1949; Eccles, 1953) that prolonged facilitation of new nervous pathways may sometimes be due to the growth of axons, or to the development of synapses. These can be seen in histological preparations as terminal buttons on the end of nerve fibres, but there is at present no evidence that their number or distribution is altered by the passage of impulses. The remarkable work of Levi-Montalcini (1961) on the substances in tissues which cause nerve growth makes this theory slightly more probable than it was.

Inhibition   When an axon has been depolarized by an excitor nerve or an excitor drug, it is for a time inexcitable. This is the cause of the refractory period which follows an impulse. The term "inhibition" is used by physiologists for the reduced excitability produced by an inhibitor nerve.

1. *Inhibition by inhibitor nerves*   This is commonly a chemically transmitted post-synaptic process, but it may also be pre-synaptic or electrical (Eccles, 1961a, 1961b, 1964). Studies of the inhibitory action of Renshaw cells in the spinal cord led to the conclusion that they release an inhibitory transmitter which causes hyperpolarization in motoneurons. This action is antagonized by strychnine (Curtis, 1963).

The occurrence of inhibitory nerves in the cerebral cortex is now clearly established (Krnjević, Randić and Straughan, 1964). GABA (γ-aminobutyric acid) has a strong depressant action on cortical neurons and it has been suggested that this substance may be the cause of this inhibition in the cortex. GABA is unlikely to be the substance liberated by Renshaw cells, since it does not antagonize the action of strychnine (Curtis, 1963).

2. *Tachyphylaxis*   Tissues may also become insensitive to drugs or transmitter without complete depolarization, and the word tachyphylaxis is used to describe this effect. When an isolated piece of smooth muscle is exposed to a drug which causes it to contract, it generally

relaxes while the drug is still in contact with the tissue. This is the phenomenon which Paton (1961) calls "fade". A similar desensitization can be shown at the motor end plate by prolonged exposure to small doses of acetylcholine applied directly (Katz and Thesleff, 1957) or released by the nerve (Thesleff, 1959).

According to Paton's theory the effect of a drug depends upon the rate at which molecules of drug combine with receptors in the tissue, rather than on the number of receptors occupied. Fade is due to the fact that this rate diminishes when most of the receptors are already saturated with the drug. According to Paton and Perry (1953), the blocking effect of nicotine on the superior cervical ganglion of a cat is at first due to depolarization, but this first effect is followed by competitive block analogous to fade. This phenomenon of fade may sometimes be specific. For example, if a large excess of tryptamine is added to a bath containing guinea pig ileum, the muscle may relax while the drug is still present. At this stage the muscle gives no response to small additional doses of tryptamine or 5-hydroxytryptamine, but gives a normal response to histamine. When the tryptamine is washed away, normal sensitivity returns in 30–60 min. (Gaddum, 1952). This phenomenon has been called specific tachyphylaxis and has been found useful in the pharmacological analysis of tissue extracts. It is generally necessary to maintain a high concentration of the desensitizing drug in the bath throughout the whole experiment. On the other hand, a large dose of other stimulating drugs may cause an unspecific desensitization of the tissue (Cantoni and Eastman, 1946; Paton, 1961). This may be part of a general property of living matter to become "habituated" to any change of conditions.

Various attempts have been made to study the mechanisms responsible for plasticity in nervous systems by sectioning nerves and studying the response of the tissue several days later. When a nerve is cut the peripheral part of the axon eventually degenerates. This is preceded by the disappearance of the chemical transmitter from the axon and by enzymic changes. For example, both choline-acetylase and acetylcholinesterase disappear from cholinergic neurons.

At the same time, the tissue on which the nerve acts may, in the course of days, become supersensitive to drugs (Cannon and Rosenblueth, 1949). This phenomenon may be the reverse of tachyphylaxis. When the nerve is intact small amounts of the transmitter are being liberated all the time, causing partial desensitization of the tissue. When this effect is removed by denervation, the tissue becomes supersensitive.

The supersensitivity is maximal when the neuron which is cut acts directly on the denervated tissue, but a smaller degree of supersensitivity occurs when the neuron acts indirectly through a synapse. This phenomenon occurs in smooth muscle, voluntary muscle, cardiac muscle, glands, melanophores and many other tissues. Cannon's "law of denervation" states "When in a series of efferent neurons, a unit is destroyed, an increased irritability to chemical agents develops in the isolated structure or structures, the effects being maximal in the part directly denervated".

The theory that this form of supersensitivity is the reverse of tachyphylaxis is supported by the work of Emmelin (1961), who found that the development of supersensitivity in the salivary gland after denervation could be diminished by the injection of pilocarpine or carbachol. These drugs are thought to take the place of acetylcholine in the gland and so to prevent the development of supersensitivity, which is attributed to the loss of the acetylcholine normally liberated by the nerves. Emmelin also showed that supersensitivity could be produced by the injection of drugs, such as atropine, which prevented the acetylcholine liberated by the nerves from combining with receptors in the tissues. The first effect of such injection is, of course, to diminish the secretion, but later when the injection of atropine ceases, supersensitivity may develop and Emmelin suggests that this is analogous to that caused by denervation. This change of sensitivity is of long duration and may perhaps be one of the mechanisms for prolonged memories.

In order to test whether this kind of supersensitivity could be produced in the spinal cord, Cannon and Haimovici (1939) carried out hemisection of the cat's spinal cord between the twelfth and thirteenth thoracic vertebræ. After an interval of 5–8 days, they injected excitor drugs, such as strychnine, acetylcholine, or sodium carbonate into the aorta, so that they were carried to the spinal cord and produced an increased effect on the quadriceps on the denervated side. They regarded this as an example of the law of denervation.

Eccles and McIntyre (1953) also produced plastic changes in the spinal cord by denervation. They sectioned cats' dorsal roots peripheral to the ganglia and then 21–40 days later stimulated the same dorsal roots and recorded the electric response in the nerves to the muscles. It might have been expected from Cannon's law that this denervation would cause supersensitivity, though less than that produced by direct denervation. The main result was, however, that mono-synaptic reflexes were depressed. This is not surprising, since Cannon's law applies only to the application of drugs; the depression might be due to disappearance of a chemical transmitter. Eccles and McIntyre point out that their results show that synapses may become defective through disuse, and effective through use, even in the spinal cord, and suggest that this may be related to facilitation in the cerebrum. This argument has been criticized as indirect. Burns' views on the very marked facilitation which he observed in the cerebrum are discussed above.

Prolonged changes in electric potential The theory that prolonged direct current changes of electric potential in the cerebral cortex were important was known among psychologists as the field theory and was believed by many people. Lashley inserted electrical conductors in the visual area of the brains of rats and found that this made no difference to their power of discriminating the shapes of objects. It was felt that such conductors would have distorted the electric field and that the field theory had been disproved.

More recent experiments have, however, given results which suggest that D.C. changes may be important (O'Leary and Goldring, 1964). Rusinov (1953) observed that a constant low level 2–10 μamp anodal current applied to the motor cortex of a rabbit produced a so-called "dominant focus of excitation". The anodal current did not itself cause excitation but, when a sensory stimulus such as a tone or light was applied during the passage of the current, a discrete movement corresponding to the polarized area occurred. This observation is, at first sight, surprising because nerves generally become excitable at the cathode rather than the anode. This effect lasted for 20–30 min. after the anodal current was switched off. These Russian results were confirmed by Morrell (1961), who summarizes later work in this field and discusses its significance. The phenomenon is interesting because the changes last longer than changes due to action potentials, and for about the same time as electrically or mechanically sensitive memory.

It is difficult to imagine that complex learning patterns can be formed by potential changes covering such large areas of cortex, but it must be remembered that the area covered depends on the experimental conditions. It might be possible to produce similar changes with a finer structure. These potential changes are presumably associated with chemical changes in the cortex and they may be important as an index of these chemical changes.

It is just possible that these changes are related to the presence of glutamate and GABA in the brain. Both of these substances are present in very high concentrations. Glutamate excites nerve cells and GABA depresses them. Under appropriate conditions these two substances can be separated from one another by paper electrophoresis at pH 6. Glutamate behaves as an acid and is carried to the anode, while GABA behaves as a base and is carried to the cathode. If this electrophoresis occurred in the brain, the region of the anode might be expected to become more excitable. On the other hand, it is doubtful whether the conditions in the brain are such as to make this change possible, but, even if this is not so, the local concentrations of glutamate and GABA may be part of the pattern of activity in the brain.

The "spreading depression" which can be produced by applying potassium to the surface of the brain (Léão, 1944; Ochs, 1962) is also associated with a surface negative potential shift, but, in this case, the direct effect is to paralyse the cortex.

Another set of experiments on DC changes in the brain have shown that a touch stimulus applied to a resting animal causes a prolonged electronegative change in the cortex. The mechanism of this is unknown, but Bremer (1961) suggested that it was due to depolarization in the dendrites (Caspers, 1961). A record of these DC changes provides an index of the wakefulness of the animal, since arousal from sleep is associated with an electronegative change. This record supplements the information provided by an electroencephalogram and may sometimes be more sensitive to small sensory stimuli.

The relation of the cerebral cortex to the rest of the brain   Views about the function of the cortex have undergone some modification in recent years. It is not the seat of consciousness. The evidence on this question was reviewed by Feldberg (1959). Animals from which the cortex has been removed appear conscious, though stupid, and they go to sleep at night. The same is true of human beings with no functional cortex. If the theory about its action discussed above is true it is more likely to be the seat of some part of the sub-conscious, which thinks original thoughts which are not necessarily related to the real world. On the other hand, it may be that the cortex performs the same function in the brain as the scientists and technicians in society. Like a computer it can predict the consequences of any given action, provided it has the relevant data. It is responsible for carrying out decisions which have been made, but the real executive power may lie with centres in the brain stem, such as the thalamus and the reticular formation, which are in touch with the hypothalamus and the limbic system, and control the sources of energy and the drive. The cerebrum provides the intellect and may suggest projects, but the brain stem decides whether these projects are worth their cost in food and energy. Schopenhauer laid emphasis on the importance of will as opposed to intelligence; it seems likely that the will resides in the brain stem.

The development of patterns in the cortex must be, to some extent, under the control of the brain stem, which alters the way they develop, and which can impose a given pattern on the cortex at short notice through the reticular formation.

Many authors felt that they would like to be able to identify some part of the brain as the seat of consciousness, and an interesting discussion of this question was published by Walshe (1957). In Carpenter's standard textbook (1853) the centre to which the most heterogeneous impressions were brought was called the "automatic apparatus": this was thought, at that time, to be situated in the medulla. The problem was discussed by Herbert Spencer and by J. Hughlings Jackson both of whom believed that the highest centre was the centre to which the most heterogeneous impressions were brought. Walshe (1957) thought that this was the seat of consciousness. He also discusses Penfield's "centrencephalic integrating system" which is based on his interpretation of the motor responses to cortical stimulation. He considers it to be "conceived in the darkness of current ignorance of the functions of the cerebral hemispheres". This ignorance may depend partly on confusion regarding the exact meaning of terms such as consciousness and mind. When this confusion has been removed the other problems may appear less formidable and less important.

VII. Memory

The first stage is the short-term memory. At any given moment it is possible to recall what has happened in the last one or two seconds, even though one may not have been listening—a fact which has been found useful in school when the master suddenly says "You are not listening; what have I just said?" There seems to be a short time during which patterns pass into the cortex before a separation is made between patterns to which attention will be paid and patterns which will be forgotten. This problem has been studied by Broadbent (1958), who measured the rate at which it is possible to transfer attention between signals arriving by different channels—for example, in the two ears. This interval is less than a second and he came to the conclusion that there must be a filter which selects one signal for attention before either of them reaches the place where learning takes place.

In the experiments of Auerbach and Correll (1961) an array of 16 letters was thrown on the retina for 0·05 sec. and this was accompanied or followed by a bar marker which indicated which letter should be reported. When the marker and the array were shown together the subjects gave the right answer in 75% of trials, but when there was an interval of only $\frac{1}{3}$ sec. between the array and the marker the score fell to 30%. The image of the array seems to have been stored for about $\frac{1}{3}$ sec. by a form of short-term memory, which is not, however, thought to be the same as that studied by Broadbent (Miller, 1963).

In a diagram ascribed to Broadbent the filter which selects sensations for attention is shown as if it were localized, but it is now suggested that this filter is spread over the whole cortex and that the first thing that happens to a sensory pattern in the cortex is that it spreads unchanged through one layer of cells. The spread of the waves from two or more sensations might be compared with the spread of the waves formed on the surface of a lake. When two stones are thrown in simultaneously, the two systems meet and cross and emerge unchanged. In the cortex the whole process lasts for a second or two, during which some mechanism records important signals and rejects unimportant signals. This possibility is suggested by the fact that the difference between important and unimportant signals may be slight. A mother may, for example, be woken by the cry of her own child but not by the cry of other children, or a man may hear his own name in a confused babble of conversation. The filter which selects such signals must be in close contact with the whole nerve net.

The surface positive discharge studied by Burns (1958) in isolated slabs of cat's cortex has already been described. This may last 0·5–5 sec., and spreads throughout the slab of cortex in one layer of cells. It is suggested that this electric change is due to the initial spread of sensory patterns responsible for the immediate memory. This pattern mostly disappears in a few seconds, except that certain features of it are selected by some mechanism in the cortex and may produce more lasting effects. Reverberating circuits (positive feedback) may play a part in this fixation.

In the second stage of memory, the cortex may be made to recapitulate the past, a hypothesis that has already been discussed. This process may be aided by proprioceptive reflexes and feedback from the sense organs; one pattern provides the proprioceptive response which is the CS for the next pattern. This type of memory is, in one sense, an acquired skill.

The main types of memory are auditory, visual and motor. Auditory memory depends to a great extent on words. One example of this is when one learns a poem by heart and can reproduce it either aloud or to oneself. Many people talk continuously to themselves during the whole of their conscious life. Auditory memory has been exploited by systems of memory training, which encourage the formation of series of words leading from one thing to another. If, for example, one wishes to remember that Mr Brown lives in Mysore Road, it is possible to say to oneself, Brown, colour, eye, myself, Mysore. The formation of such series is an art which can be learned and is efficient. The absurdity of the relation between one word and the next is no disadvantage since it makes memory easier, but the intermediate words can soon be forgotten, since a direct connexion is formed between the first and last words (Brown and Mysore). Most people do not use such elaborate methods, but remember directly by saying the first and last word over to themselves several times. This kind of memory is partly auditory and partly motor. Other types of memory or skill, such as remembering how to ride a bicycle, are more purely motor.

Visual memory may be remarkably efficient. Some people can recite whole books by visualizing one page after another. Those who are blind and deaf may develop memories based on touch and smell and other senses.

In the present state of knowledge any theory about the storage of memories must be speculative and is likely to appear improbable. Plastic nerve nets are, by their very nature, unsuited for the prolonged storage of memories. There must be some mechanism by which a record is kept in the brain of the patterns which have formed in the cerebrum. The amount of information is very large and it must be stored in some form of code. It is generally believed that this code is chemical; and depends on the structure of specific proteins, or of molecules of ribonucleic acid (RNA), which might then determine the structure of specific proteins.

According to the theories discussed above, an idea is associated with a pattern which is both spatial and temporal. It is formed by impulses in sensory nerves and depends on a complex system of time intervals between these impulses. The same pattern could be formed again by the same system of impulses. On the other hand, an idea could also be defined in terms of the distribution activity at any one moment. Very little information can be stored as action potentials, since the wave length of an action potential, even in a slow fibre, is several millimetres and there will seldom be more than one in a neuron at a time, but the pattern may depend on the depolarization of neurons.

It has been suggested that the release of antibodies with specific actions on some brain cells, but not on others, may form patterns of activity in the brain. Some evidence for this view was obtained by Mihailović and his colleagues (1961, 1964) who prepared antibodies by injecting extracts of the caudate nucleus of cats into rabbits. In one series of experiments the rabbit serum was then injected into the lateral cerebral ventricle of cats over a period of days and it caused changes in the electroencephalogram, localized in the caudate nucleus; in another series of experiments it caused, within four hours, a rise in the amount of a histamine-like substance in extracts of the caudate nucleus, but not in the hippocampus. In parallel experiments antigens to the hippocampus caused a rise of histamine-like substance in the hippocampus, but not in the caudate nucleus.

It has been suggested that this gross difference between two large structures in a cat's brain may be an extreme example of an important mechanism, and that every cell in the brain may be antigenically different from every other cell. If this is so, long-term memories could perhaps be roused by the release of suitable antibodies which would impose the appropriate pattern. The actual store of memories could be kept in code as molecules of protein, or of RNA, but it is difficult to imagine how this code could be formed, although it is likely to be a slow process, used only for long-term memories.

Various people have suggested that this code is similar to the genetic code and depends on the arrangement of bases in a molecule of RNA. This theory is attractive because it might provide a common mechanism for the storage of instincts and learning. The inherited behaviour patterns known as instincts are likely to be transmitted by the RNA code, and this increases the likelihood that the acquired behaviour patterns known as learning depend on the same mechanism. Many people feel that some such theory must be valid, but evidence on the subject is indirect and unconvincing (Morrell, 1961; Hydén, 1962; Gerard, 1964). The site and mode of action of the memory code is unknown.

References

Adrian, E. D. (1936), *J. Physiol., Lond.*, **88**, 127.
Adrian, E. D. and Matthews, B. H. C. (1934), *Brain*, **57**, 355.
Ashby, W. R. (1954), *Design for a Brain*, Chapman & Hall, London.
Auerbach, E. and Correll, A. S. (1961), *Bull. Syst. Tech. J.*, **40**, 309.
Beurle, R. L. (1957), *Phil. Trans. B*, **240**, 55.
Bowden, B. V. (1962), *Advanc. Sci.*, **18**, 543.
Bremer, F. (1961), In *The Nature of Sleep (Ciba Symp.)*, p. 30, (Edited by G. E. W. Wolstenholme and C. M. O'Connor), Churchill, London.
Broadbent, D. E. (1958), *Perception and Communication*, Pergamon Press, London.
Brobeck, J. R. (1960), In *Handbook of Physiology*, Sect. I, Vol. II, (Edited by J. Field, American Physiological Society, Washington.
Burns, B. D. (1958), *The Mammalian Cerebral Cortex*, Arnold, London.
Burns, B. D. and Smith, G. K. (1962), *J. Physiol., Lond.*, **164**, 238.
Cannon, W. B. (1915), *Bodily Changes in Fear, Hunger, Pain and Rage*, Appleton, New York.
Cannon, W. B. and Haimovici, H. (1939), *Amer. J. Physiol.*, **126**, 731.
Cannon, W. B. and Rosenblueth, A. (1949), *The Supersensitivity of Denervated Structures*, Macmillan, New York.
Cantoni, G. L. and Eastman, C. (1946), *J. Pharmacol.*, **87**, 393.
Carpenter, W. B. (1853), *Principles of Human Physiology*, 4th Ed., Churchill, London.
Caspers, H. (1961), In *The Nature of Sleep (Ciba Symp.)*, p. 237 (Edited by C. E. W. Wolstenholme and C. M. O'Connor), Churchill, London.
Curtis, D. R. (1963), *Pharmacol. Rev.*, **15**, 333.
Delafresnaye, J. F. (1961), *Brain Mechanisms and Learning*, Blackwell, Oxford.
Doty, R. W. (1961), Discussion in *Brain Mechanisms and Learning*, p. 659 (Edited by J. F. Delafresnaye,), Blackwell, Oxford.
Dudel, J. and Kuffler, S. W. (1961), *J. Physiol., Lond.*, **155**, 514.
Eccles, J. C. (1953), *The Neurophysiological Basis of Mind*, Clarendon Press, Oxford.
Eccles, J. C. (1958), In *Neurological Basis of Behaviour (Ciba Symp.)*, p. 28 (Edited by G. E. W. Wolstenholme, and C. M. O'Connor), Churchill, London.
Eccles, J. C. (1961a), *Proc. roy. Soc. B*, **153**, 445.
Eccles, J. C. (1961b), *Ergebn. Physiol.*, **51**, 300.
Eccles, J. C. (1964), *The Physiology of Synapsis*, Springer, Berlin.
Eccles, J. C. and McIntyre, A. K. (1953), *J. Physiol., Lond.*, **121**, 492.
Emmelin, N. (1961), *Pharmacol. Rev.*, **13**, 17.
Feldberg, W. (1959), *Brit. med. J.*, **2**, 771.
Fisher, R. A. (1959), *Statistical Methods and Scientific Inference*, Oliver & Boyd, Edinburgh.
Frisch, K. von (1962), *Erinnerungen eines Biologen*, Springer, Berlin.
Gaddum, J. H. (1952), *J. Physiol., Lond.*, **119**, 363.
Gaddum, J. H. (1956), In *Extrasensory Perception (Ciba Symp.)*, p. 38 (Edited by G. E. W. Wolstenholme, and C. M. O'Connor), Churchill, London.
Gaddum, J. H. (1963), *Nature, Lond.*, **197**, 741.
Gerard, R. W. (1964), In *Neurophysiology*, Vol. 3, p. 1919 (Edited by J. Field), American Physiological Society, New York.
Grossman, S. P. (1960), *Science*, **132**, 301.
Harris, G. W., Michael, R. P. and Scott, P. P. (1958), In *Neurological Basis of Behaviour (Ciba Symp.)*, pp. 236 and 252 (Edited by G. E. W. Wolstenholme, and C. M. O'Connor), Churchill, London.
Hebb, D. O. (1949), *The Organization of Behaviour*, Chapman & Hall, London.
Hess, W. R. (1957), *The Functional Organization of the Diencephalon*, Grune & Stratton, New York.
Hubel, D. H. and Wiesel, T. N. (1962), *J. Physiol., Lond.*, **160**, 106.
Hughes, J. R. (1958), *Physiol. Rev.*, **38**, 91.

Hull, C. L. (1951), *Essentials of Behavior*, Yale University Press, New Haven.
Hydén, H. (1962), *Endeavour*, **21**, 144.
Katz, B. (1958), *Bull. Johns Hopk. Hosp.*, **102**, 275.
Katz, B. and Thesleff, S. (1957), *J. Physiol., Lond.*, **138**, 63.
Köhler, W. (1925), *The Mentality of Apes* (English translation by E. Winter) 1957, Penguin Books, London.
Köhler, W. (1930), *Gestalt Psychology*, Bell, London.
Konorski, J. (1948), *Conditioned Reflexes and Neuron Organization*, Cambridge University Press, London.
Krnjević, K. and Phillis, J. W. (1962), *J. Physiol., Lond.*, **166**, 296.
Krnjević, K., Randić, M. and Straughan, D. W. (1964), *Nature, Lond.*, **201**, 1294.
Lashley, K. S. (1929), *Brain Mechanisms and Intelligence: A Quantitative Study of Injuries to the Brain*, University of Chicago Press, Chicago.
Léão, A. A. P. (1944), *J. Neurophysiol.*, **7**, 359.
Levi-Montalcini, R. (1961), *Quart. Rev. Biol.*, **36**, 99.
Livingston, R. B. (1959), In *Neurophysiology*, p. 741 (Edited by J. Field), American Physiological Society, Washington.
Lloyd, D. P. C. (1949), *J. gen. Physiol.*, **33**, 147.
Locke, J. (1690), *An Essay Concerning Humane Understanding*, 1947 Ed., Everyman, London.
Lorente de No, R. (1939), *J. Neurophysiol.*, **2**, 402.
Lorenz, K. (1952), *King Solomon's Ring* (Translated by M. K. Wilson), Methuen, London.
Magnes, J., Moruzzi, G. and Pompeiano, O. (1961), In *The Nature of Sleep (Ciba Symp.)*, p. 57 (Edited by G. E. W. Wolstenholme and C. M. O'Connor), Churchill, London.
Mihailović, Lj. and Janković, B. D. (1961), *Nature, Lond.*, **197**, 665.
Mihailović, Lj., Janković, B. D., Beleslin, B., Mitrović, K. and Krzalić, Lj. (1964), *Nature, Lond.*, **203**, 763.
Miller, N. E. (1960), *Fed. Proc.*, **19**, 846.
Miller, N. E. (1961), *Bull. N.Y. Acad. Sci.*, **92**, 830.
Miller, N. E. (1963), *Proc. roy. Soc. B*, **158**, 481.
Miller, N. E. (1964), In *Animal Behaviour and Drug Action (Ciba Symp.)*, p. 1–22 (Edited by H. Steinberg), Churchill, London.
Milne, L. J. and Milne, M. J. G. (1963), *The Senses of Animals and Men*, Deutsch, London.
Morrell, F. (1961), *Physiol. Rev.*, **41**, 443.
Myers, R. E. (1956), *Brain*, **79**, 358.
Ochs, S. (1962), *Int. Rev. Neurobiol.*, **4**, 1.
Olds, J. (1962), *Physiol. Rev.* **42**, 554.
O'Leary, J. L. and Goldring, S. (1964), *Physiol. Rev.*, **44**, 91.
Paton, W. D. M. (1961), *Proc. roy. Soc. B*, **154**, 21.
Paton, W. D. M. and Perry, W. L. M. (1953), *J. Physiol., Lond.*, **19**, 43.
Pavlov, I. P. (1927), *Conditional Reflexes* (Translated by G. V. Anrep,), Oxford University Press, London.
Razran, G. (1961), *Psychol. Rev.*, **68**, 81.
Rheinberger, M. and Jasper, H. H. (1937), *Amer. J. Physiol.*, **119**, 186.
Rosenblatt, F. (1962), *Principles of Neurodynamics*, Spartan Books, U.S.A.
Rusinov, V. S. (1953), *Commun. XIX Int. Physiol. Congr.*, Montreal.
Scott, J. P. (1962), In *The Behaviour of Domestic Animals*, p. 3 (Edited by E. S. E. Hafez), Baillière, Tindall & Cox, London.
Senden, M. von (1960), *Space and Sight. The Perception of Space and Shape on the Congenitally Blind Before and After Operation* (Translated by P. Heath), Free Press of Glencoe, New York.
Sherrington, C. S. (1946), *Man on his Nature*, Cambridge University Press, London.
Skinner, B. F. (1938), *The Behaviour of Organisms. An Experimental Analysis*, Appleton, New York.
Sperry, R. W. (1956), *Psychological Plasticity and Brain Circuit Theory* (Edited by H. F. Harlow and C. N. Woolsey), University of Wisconsin Press (Quoted by B. D. Burns).
Stein, L. (1964), In *Animal Behaviour and Drug Action (Ciba Symp.)*, p. 91 (Edited by H. Steinberg), Churchill, London.

Steinberg, H. (1964), *Brit. med. Bull.*, **20**, 75.
Thesleff, S. (1959), *J. Physiol., Lond.*, **148**, 659.
Thorpe, W. H. (1963), *Learning and Instinct in Animals*, 2nd Ed., Methuen, London.
Tinbergen, N. (1951), *The Study of Instinct*, Clarendon Press, Oxford.
Uttley, A. M. (1955), *Proc. roy. Soc. B*, **144**, 229.
Walshe, F. M. R. (1957), *Brain*, **80**, 510.
Walter, W. G. (1953), *The Living Brain*, Duckworth, London.
Wooldridge, D. E. (1963), *The Machinery of the Brain*, McGraw-Hill, New York.
Young, J. Z. (1961), *Biol. Rev.*, **36**, 32.

Biochemical Aspects of Memory

Derek Richter

In considering the biochemical aspects of memory it may be useful to look first at one particular aspect, the element of retention which has been described as the "memory trace" or "engram". When an animal learns, its reactions to a stimulus become changed for an appreciable period of time. Sensory impulses reaching the brain produce an altered pattern of neuronal discharge, and we conclude that something in the brain has changed. Richard Semon defined the engram broadly as "a permanent change wrought by a stimulus on any living substance". Nervous tissue appears to be specially adapted for undergoing modification of this kind, and the changes occurring are specific in the sense that each type of stimulus evokes a characteristic pattern of response. The increase in knowledge and skill that occurs in each of us between birth and maturity is sufficient evidence of the enormous capacity of the brain for acquiring engrams by undergoing this highly specific kind of plastic change.

What then exactly is the nature of an engram? Physiologists have commonly thought in terms of the plasticity of neuronal nets and the properties of their synaptic connexions. Other investigators have thought that excitation might bring about a specific change in a chemical substance such as the nucleic acid or protein molecules in the nerve cells. These two views are not necessarily incompatible, for synaptic transmission is effected by chemical transmitters, and any permanent change at the synapse is likely to involve a biochemical reaction. The main question is what determines the specificity of the signal. Is it determined by the structure of a chemical molecule or by the characteristics of a neuronal net? In other words, is the engram coded at a molecular or at a cellular level? This is a central problem in this field of investigation.

The nature of the engram can be studied in a number of different ways. One way is to examine the biochemical changes which occur in nervous tissues when they are stimulated. We can also study the changes in single nerve cells by histochemical procedures. Of special interest in this connexion are the nucleic acids and proteins which belong to the structural elements of the cell. Another approach is to study in animal experiments the effects on learning of drugs and enzyme inhibitors which influence biochemical processes in the brain. In this chapter some of the biochemical evidence obtained in these ways is discussed and biochemical hypotheses of memory are considered.

I. Effects of Stimulation on Nervous Tissues

Biochemical changes in the brain   Whatever the nature of an engram may be, it is by definition something that results from applying a stimulus. It may also be associated with a chemical change. The problem can therefore be approached by applying stimuli to nervous tissues and looking for any changes in the chemical substances they contain.

One of the difficulties in chemical work with nervous tissues is the extreme rapidity of post-mortem change, but this can be largely prevented, and information about the chemical composition of the brain during life can be obtained by the chemical analysis of nervous tissue taken from rats or other small animals instantly killed by immersion in liquid air. The intense cold freezes the brain solid in a few seconds and can fix biochemical changes which are too transient to be observed by other means. In this way it has been shown that electrical stimulation of the brain causes a rapid release of the synaptic transmitter substance acetylcholine (Richter and Crossland, 1949). This gives evidence of increased neuronal activity, which is indicated also by a rapid breakdown of "high-energy" phosphate esters and the formation of lactic acid, inorganic phosphate and ammonia (Richter and Dawson, 1948; Dawson and Richter, 1950a). These changes in the labile constituents of the cell take place within a few seconds of applying a stimulus and are rapidly reversible: within a very short time the metabolites return to their normal levels. Similar changes in the acetylcholine and lactic acid of the brain were shown to occur when animals were excited under normal physiological conditions. The rapid changes in brain acetylcholine and other labile metabolites on stimulation have been confirmed directly (Ridge, 1961; Warren and Schenker, 1960) and also in physiological experiments in which the subarachnoid space was perfused with saline and measurements were made of metabolites diffusing out from the surface of the brain: stimulation greatly increased the output of acetylcholine in the perfusion fluid (MacIntosh and Oborin, 1953). In similar experiments it has recently been found that increased cortical activity is associated with an increased level of glutamate and a decreased level of *gamma*-aminobutyrate (GABA) in the perfusion fluid from the cortex of the brain (Jasper, Khan and Elliott, 1965). These changes in glutamate and GABA are of interest in view of their properties as modifiers of neuronal activity in the central nervous system.

Small changes *in vivo* in the amount of any of the main constituents of nervous tissue, such as the lipids or structural proteins, cannot easily be detected by the usual methods of chemical analysis: but by administering a metabolite labelled with a radioactive isotope and measuring the rate of incorporation, it is possible to detect a change in the rate of synthesis although there is no significant bulk change. Experiments with radioactive phosphorus (^{32}P) as a tracer showed that phospholipids are normally synthesized at an appreciable rate *in vivo* in the mouse brain (Dawson and Richter, 1950b). Stimulation caused a significant decrease

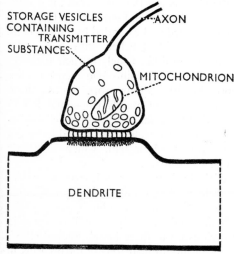

STORAGE VESICLES
CONTAINING
TRANSMITTER
SUBSTANCES

AXON

MITOCHONDRION

DENDRITE

Fig. 1. Diagram showing a section of a synapse.

in the rate of incorporation of ^{32}P into phospholipid; a decrease was observed whether the brain was stimulated electrically or by inducing excitement under physiological conditions. In these experiments excitement was induced by putting the animals in a slowly rotating metal drum. It could be shown that the change in phospholipid turnover was not due to concomitant muscular exercise, since it was absent in animals previously conditioned to running in the drum. It has been reported that stimulation also decreases the rate of incorporation of ^{32}P into peripheral nerve and sensory ganglia (Samuels *et al*., 1951); but in the superior cervical ganglion (which contains cholinergic synapses) Larrabee and Leicht (1965) have recently found that stimulation of the preganglionic nerve causes a selective increase in labelling of phosphatidylinositol. The increased labelling on stimulation was blocked by tubocurarine which blocks synaptic transmission and the effect could be reproduced by applying eserine and acetylcholine. They conclude that the increased labelling of phosphatidylinositol when the pre-ganglionic nerve is stimulated is a specific effect produced by the trans-mitter substances on the post-synaptic nerve cell.

Protein synthesis   Measurements of the rate of incorporation of labelled amino acids showed that under normal conditions *in vivo* there is a relatively high rate of turnover of proteins in the brain (Gaitonde and Richter, 1953; 1956). The overall rate of protein synthesis was found to be greater in young animals than in adults and autoradiographic studies with [^{35}S]methionine gave evidence that incorporation of amino acids into protein is more active in the grey matter than the white: it is most active in the cell bodies of the nerve cells (Cohn, Gaitonde and Richter, 1954). These observations were confirmed and extended by Lajtha *et al.* (1957) in experiments using amino acids labelled with radioactive carbon. Individual proteins in the brain differ widely in their turnover rate. The protein giving the highest rate of amino acid incorporation was identified as a liponucleoprotein with staining properties like those of the nucleoprotein aggregates (containing mainly ribosomal RNA) identified by histologists in the Nissl material of the nerve cell bodies (Clouet and Richter, 1958): this liponucleoprotein was found to have a half-life of about 90 minutes. Proteolipid protein, which is mainly present in myelin, had a low rate of turnover.

The overall rate of turnover of the brain proteins varies to some extent with the physiological state: the rate of incorporation of [^{35}S]methionine was found to be reduced in narcosis and in insulin hypoglycæmia. Electrical stimulation of the brain produced only a small decrease in labelling of brain proteins in periods up to three hours. Shapot (1957) found a decreased incorporation of amino acid into brain proteins in rats excited by teasing them, but other investigators have reported an increase or no effect (Palladin, 1957; Dingman, Sporn and Davies, 1959). The changes in amino acid incorporation produced by stimula-tion are not always easy to interpret, since stimulation of the brain may cause changes in cell permeability, size of the amino acid pool and blood circulation: electrical stimulation may also lead to anoxia by interfering with the respiratory centre. Further, the data reported by different investigators are not always comparable, since some data have not been corrected for changes in specific activity of free amino acid in the brain.

In long-term experiments in which rats were reared in different environments Bennett *et al.* (1964) found that constant exposure to sensory stimulation increased the overall weight and protein content of the cerebral cortex in comparison with control animals kept under conditions of minimal stimulation. Increased protein synthesis in the stimulated animals was indicated not only by the overall protein content but also by the increase in proteins with enzymic activity, such as cholinesterase.

There is some evidence that stimulation can cause changes in the chemical properties of individual proteins of brain and nerve. Electrical stimulation of the brain was reported to cause partial denaturation of brain proteins and an increase in the proportion of protein-bound SH groups: the staining properties of the proteins were also found to be changed (Ungar and Romano, 1962; Fischer, Zeman and Irons, 1961; Freundl, Gerlach and Turba, 1964). Vrba and Folbergrova (1959) reported a small decrease in the protein-bound amide groups in proteins of the rat brain after prolonged physical exercise and a similar finding has been reported for peripheral nerve (Jakoubek *et al.*, 1963). Stimulation by administration of camphor was found to increase the incorporation of ^{32}P into phosphoproteins of the brain *in vivo* (Vladimirov, 1953) and incorporation of ^{32}P was increased in brain slices stimulated electrically *in vitro* (Heald, 1959): the phosphoproteins of the nerve cell are located mainly in the cell membranes and it is possible that they may be concerned in the transport of electrolytes across the cell membrane.

Studies of protein metabolism in peripheral nerve have given evidence that axoplasm generated in the cell body of the neuron passes into the axon where it moves outwards as a cohesive column advancing at a rate of about 1 mm. a day. An outward flow of axoplasm was suggested by earlier investigations which showed a damming of the flow in constricted nerve fibres, and it was confirmed by experiments in which the axoplasm was labelled with ^{32}P (Grande and Richter, 1950; Samuels *et al.*, 1951; Miani, 1963): the rate of flow was found to be increased by electrical stimulation. More recent observations of the movement of a specific protein, choline acetyltransferase, in motor fibres of the goat sciatic nerve have shown that the flow of protein in the axon is not entirely free, but the protein is apparently associated with a carrier membrane system (Hebb and Silver, 1965). The outward flow of protein has also been shown by applying [^3H]leucine to small groups of neurons and observing by autoradiographic methods the advance along the nerve fibres of the travelling crest of labelled protein (Weiss and Taylor, 1965). It has been suggested that protein synthesized continuously in the cell body is broken down in distal parts of the axon by neutral proteinase and utilized to provide amino acid substrates for the metabolic activity of the nerve (Richter, 1962). Stimulation of peripheral nerve causes ammonia to be liberated and an increase in the amount of protein broken down in association with increased activity of the neutral proteinase (Jakoubek *et al.*, 1963). There is also evidence that "trophic" substances, which may be polypeptides, are liberated at the myoneural endings of peripheral nerves (Gutmann, 1964).

From these investigations it would appear that (a) the overall rate of protein turnover is relatively high in nervous tissues, and particularly in the nerve cell bodies; and that (b) there is a regular net synthesis in the nerve cell bodies of proteins which pass out into the axons: the brain is therefore essentially a neurosecretory organ. Stimulation causes the liberation of transmitter substances and an increased energy requirement associated with rapid reversible changes in a number of labile metabolites. The overall rate of protein turnover is not greatly affected by stimulation in acute experiments, but prolonged stimulation appears to increase the rate of generation of axoplasm and it affects the rate of incorporation of metabolites into some of the structural elements of the nerve cell. There is some evidence from long-term experiments that sensory stimulation can increase the total quantity of structural and other proteins in the rat brain.

Ribonucleic acid (RNA) metabolism

Chromatolysis The earlier literature contains many references to changes in the nerve cell bodies, described as "chromatolysis", which may result from conditions such as prolonged stimulation or administration of toxic substances. Dolley (1913) reported changes in size, shape, nuclear position and appearance of the cytoplasm of Purkinje cells in the cerebellum of dogs after they had been exercised in a treadmill. Particularly characteristic was the reduction in the amount of RNA-containing particles (Nissl substance) in the cytoplasm of the cell bodies. However, Köcher (1916) carried out a similar series of experiments in which he failed to find any consistent changes attributable to stimulation: he found only a variable number of cells showing chromatolysis in tissues taken from both experimental and control animals. He pointed out the many sources of error in the fixing and staining procedures, and especially the post-mortem changes that take place between the time of death and the penetration of the tissue by the fixing agents. He concluded that previous investigators had drawn their conclusions from an insufficient number of experiments. The experiments of Hydén (1943), who determined the RNA content of nerve cell bodies by measuring their ultra-violet absorption, and of Bertram and Barr (1949), appeared to give evidence of a depletion of nucleoproteins and other proteins after electrical stimulation. However, Liu, Bailey and Windle (1950) re-investigated the effects of stimulation, using a rapid perfusion method of fixation to minimize post-mortem change. In a series of carefully controlled experiments designed to repeat Hydén's work, they failed to find any change whatever in the Nissl pattern of spinal ganglion cells after prolonged electrical stimulation at a physiological level. They were able to produce chromatolysis only with strong non-physiological electrical stimuli exceeding 20 volts or by clamping a nerve for eight hours. These experiments showed that chromatolysis can be produced by powerful stimulation, but suggested that it is a consequence of cell injury rather than a normal response to physiological stimulation.

Changes in RNA shown by chemical methods   The nerve cell contains several different kinds of nucleic acids. Apart from the deoxyribonucleic acids (DNA) in the nucleus, most of the nucleic acids are in the RNA of the ribosomes and polysomes: but there are also appreciable amounts of soluble (transfer) RNAs and nuclear (messenger) RNAs some of which are relatively labile. Brain tissue thus contains RNAs which differ in molecular weight, base ratio and lability as well as in

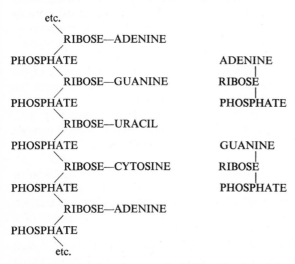

Fig. 2. Representation of a part of a RNA molecule and free nucleotides.

distribution and function in relation to protein synthesis. The concentration of RNA is highest in the body of the nerve cell, but it is present also in the axon and dendrites. Since the cell body is only a small part of the nerve cell (in many cells less than 5 %) the amount of RNA in the cell body may be less than a quarter of that in the whole cell (Edström, Eichner and Edström, 1962). It is clear that local changes in the RNA of the cell body are not necessarily representative of changes in the cell as a whole or in the whole tissue. Nervous tissues contain active polymerases capable of forming RNA from nucleotides: they also contain ribonucleases which break down RNA. In cell injury or post-mortem autolysis the RNA content of the cell can undergo rapid change.

  Cohen (1962) concluded that chromatolysis might represent a physical change in the staining properties or distribution of the RNA rather than

a change in quantity of RNA. However, toxic stimulants such as picrotoxin, strychnine, leptazol and tetanus toxin, which produce chromatolysis, apparently cause a breakdown of RNA in nervous tissues (Sikdar
and Ghosh, 1964; Chitre, Chopra and Talwar, 1964). Determination of
the base ratio in RNA extracted from frozen brain tissue showed that
convulsions were accompanied by a significant increase in the adenine:
uridine (A/U) ratio (Talwar and Chitre, 1965). This does not imply a
change in the coding of the RNA, but rather the formation of a normal
RNA containing a higher proportion of adenine, or formation of
polyadenylic acid by polymerization of adenylic acid resulting from
breakdown of adenosine triphosphate (ATP). Prolonged stimulation
from an epileptogenic focus can result in the development of a secondary
"mirror focus" in which the nerve cell bodies show increased staining
for RNA: but it is doubtful whether the increased staining indicates an
increase in the net amount of RNA (Morrell, 1962). Geiger, Yamasaki
and Lyons (1956) obtained rapidly frozen samples of brain tissue by
applying a cooled metal cylinder directly to the cerebral cortex of the
anæsthetized cat; they found that stimulation of the cortex through the
brachial plexus for 5–20 sec. produced a rapid breakdown of nucleic
acids, but the change was rapidly reversible. These experiments give
evidence that at least part of the RNA in the brain is labile and capable
of undergoing rapid change as a result of stimulation.

Histochemical and cytochemical investigations   Hamberger and Hydén
(1949) and Brattgård (1952) studied the effect of physiological stimulation on the RNA content of individual nerve cell bodies in tissue sections
after fixation in Carnoy's solution, and they obtained evidence of a
biphasic change: they found an initial *increase* in RNA after mild or
brief stimulation for periods of the order of 10 min. to 1 hour followed
in some cases by a fall if stimulation was sufficiently intense. Other
investigators have also reported rapid changes in the RNA content of
retinal ganglion cells when stimulated by light (Chentsov, Boroviagin
and Brodskii, 1961). Brattgård used an improved method of estimating
RNA in the cells by measuring the X-ray absorption before and after
extracting the RNA with ribonuclease. His experiments included a
comparison of the nucleoprotein and protein content of retinal ganglion
cells from rabbits living in daylight and animals reared in darkness. The
ganglion cells from animals reared in darkness were small and lacked the
normal complement of RNA and protein. From this it appeared that
adequate physiological stimulation over a fairly long period of time is
needed for the normal development of the retinal ganglion cell.

Hydén and Pigon (1960) determined the RNA and protein in the
bodies of large Deiters' nerve cells removed by microdissection from
the vestibular nucleus of the rabbit. Stimulation of the vestibular nerve
by rotating the animals for 25 min. a day for 7 days caused an increase

of 4·5% in the mean RNA content ($\mu\mu$g/cell body) and an increase of 14% in the mean dry weight of the cell bodies. The activity of oxidative enzymes also increased, Reverse changes in the RNA content and enzymic activity of the neighbouring glial cells were noted. Changes in RNA after brief periods of stimulation were not reported in these experiments.

In another series of investigations Hydén and Egyházi (1962, 1963, 1964) determined the RNA content and base composition in the bodies of Deiters' cells in the rat brain after stimulation by rotating the animals for 25 min. twice daily for 4 days. The effects of this form of stimulation were compared with those obtained in a second group of

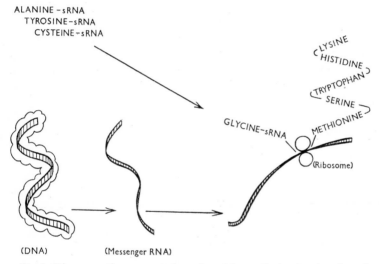

Fig. 3. Diagrammatic representation of protein synthesis, showing the roles of DNA, messenger RNA, transfer or soluble RNA (sRNA) and ribosomes.

animals deprived of a ready supply of food and made to climb up a steel wire to get food. Since this was a difficult task it introduced an element of learning. They found that the RNA content of the cell bodies increased by 6–10% in both groups of stimulated animals in comparison with controls. In neither group was there any significant change in base composition of the cytoplasmic (mainly ribosomal) RNA, but there was an increase in the adenine : uracil (A/U) ratio in the mixture of nuclear (mainly messenger) RNAs in the group made to climb a wire to get their food. However, the change in base ratio was not specific for the nerve cells, since a comparable change in the adenine : guanine (A/G) ratio was found also in the nuclear RNA of neighbouring glial cells.

In a further experiment rats accustomed to using one front paw for procuring their food were forced by the shape of the container to use the other front paw. Here again an element of learning was involved and, since "handedness" is to some extent localized on the corresponding side of the brain, it was possible to look for changes in the RNA of nerve cells on the "experimental" side while the opposite side served as a control. They found that over a period of 4 days the RNA content of the bodies of cortical neurons increased by 22% on the "experimental" side of the brain and there was also a change in base composition with an increase in the ratio $(A + G)/(C + U)$. In more recent experiments Hydén and Lange (1965) have reported that the RNA produced at the start of a learning experiment is rich in adenine and uracil, whereas later there is an increase in RNA of a ribosomal type.

Edström and his colleagues have studied the effects of stimulation on a number of different types of nerve cell. Using improved analytical procedures, Edström (1964a) showed that the RNA in the axon of the Mauthner neuron of the goldfish is of ribosomal type: this indicates that protein may be synthesized locally in the axon as well as in the body of the neuron. The cell body of a neuron normally reacts to experimental cutting of the axon by increased formation of RNA and protein. They found that the RNA content of the cell body remained constant during regeneration in spite of the change in aggregation associated with "chromatolysis"; but there was a rapid change in base composition of the RNA in the severed axon with a marked increase in the A/G ratio (Edström, 1964b). Physiological stimulation of the Mauthner neuron by rotating the fish for periods of 30–90 min. caused a *decrease* of more than 40% in the RNA content of the axon (Jakoubek and Edström, 1965). Electrical stimulation of the stretch receptor neuron of the lobster *in vitro* for periods of 1–6 hours was without effect on the RNA content of the cell body or on labelling of RNA with ^{32}P. Experiments of short duration gave some evidence of a rapid change in base composition and relative increase in a labile adenine-rich fraction, but this was not observed if stimulation was continued for 24 hours. The physiological activity of the neuron was not affected by inhibiting the synthesis of RNA with actinomycin-D (Grampp and Edström, 1963; Edström and Grampp, 1965).

What conclusions can be drawn from these apparently contradictory results? Most of the evidence up to now is consistent with the view that axonal proteins required for functional activity are synthesized mainly in the cell body. Increased functional activity can increase the protein requirement of the axon and under some conditions it can increase the synthesis of RNA and protein in the cell body: this is suggested, for example, by the experiments of Hydén and Pigon (1960) in which increased neuronal activity is associated with an increase in oxidative enzymes and also in the content of RNA. But stimulation did not increase the amount of RNA in the Mauthner neuron of the goldfish, or in the lobster stretch receptor neuron or in the experiments of Liu,

Bailey and Windle (1950) on various mammals. It seems therefore that stimulation and increase in RNA do not necessarily go together. A distinction must be made between short-term responses and long-term effects on RNA. Some of the RNA is relatively labile and can undergo rapid change. We do not yet know what factors determine the levels of different RNA fractions *in vivo* in the cell, but it is known that many cells contain homopolymerases; and a relatively small amount of a homopolymer such as polyadenylic acid is enough to change the base ratio of an RNA fraction without specific recoding of RNA.

The studies of Hydén and Egyházi (1964) of changes in RNA associated with learning are attractive in the ingenuity and originality of the experimental approach. However, the possibility must be considered that other factors including stress due to deprivation of food, agonal factors such as anoxia at the time of death, and post-mortem changes prior to fixation of the tissue, may be as important as the learning in these experiments. Changes in quantity and base composition of RNA have been observed after administration of leptazol and other substances, with or without noticeable signs of change in nervous activity: such changes in RNA also occur in cells other than nerve cells. It would therefore appear that changes in the RNA and proteins of the nerve cell body are not specific for learning.

II. Biochemical Factors that Influence Learning and Memory

Nutritional factors and drugs Information about the mechanisms concerned in learning and memory can be obtained by studying the effects of biochemical factors which influence these processes. The brain is more resistant than most organs to the effects of dietary insufficiency, but it has been noted that rats kept for 4–6 months on a protein-deficient diet perform less well in learning tests than normally fed controls. Reduced learning ability was found to be associated with reduced levels of free GABA and of enzymes concerned with glutamate metabolism in the brain; the effect was reversible to some extent by restoring protein to the diet (Rajalakshmi *et al.*, 1965). In animal experiments of this kind it is difficult to know which aspect of memory is affected. Clinical experience with human subjects has shown that protein deficiency is associated with general mental apathy, difficulty in concentrating and lack of drive; this might be the reason for the poor performance in memory tests. An impairment of learning ability associated with reduced levels of serotonin (5-hydroxytryptamine) in the brain has been reported in experiments in which puppies were fed from birth on a diet enriched with phenylalanine (Himwich, Dravid and Berk, 1965). There have been reports that learning in animals and man can be improved by administering nucleic acids (Cook *et al.*, 1963); but the brain can synthesize nucleotides and RNA from formate, glycine, orotic acid and other precursors, and it is unlikely that RNA in the diet can enter directly into the nerve cells. Much better authenticated are the effects on memory of a lack of thiamin (vitamin B_1). In human subjects chronic thiamin deficiency causes beri beri, but acute deprivation can produce the Korsakov syndrome (Wernicke's encephalopathy) in which a characteristic feature is a selective loss of memory for recent events. Since "immediate" memory (for retention spans of about a minute) may be relatively unimpaired, the defect appears to be mainly in the process of consolidation by which a temporary impression is converted into a more permanent memory trace. Another form of memory defect sometimes seen in this condition is false recall, in which an intended word is unintentionally replaced by a word of similar sound, for example "consecrate" for "concentrate" or "bottle" for "bottom". In thiamin deficiency the blood pyruvate is commonly raised and there is evidence that the energy metabolism of nervous tissues is deranged, but the characteristic memory defect may be due to impaired neuronal function which is secondary to vascular changes in the region of the mamillary bodies and hypothalamus rather than to a primary biochemical lesion in the nerve cells (Brierley, 1966).

Many toxic compounds produce confusional states in which there are varying degrees of memory impairment; this can be of consequence in the case of drugs such as barbiturates with which the loss of memory can result in a patient taking an overdose. Barbiturate anæsthesia has been used to measure the time required for memory consolidation in animal experiments. It has been shown, for example in the rat, that learned material is obliterated by anæsthetic drugs administered within about 20 min. of learning, but after longer periods the memory survives anæsthesia with pentobarbitone, ether and other agents. Hyoscine (scopolamine) appears to act selectively to some extent in reducing retention or recall in human subjects: thus patients given hyoscine during childbirth may be fully conscious at the time, but may have little recollection of it afterwards. Marihuana has been reported to have a selective action on memory recall: those who have experienced this effect report that the whole of the past may be forgotten at once, so that the present does not appear to arise out of the past (Beringer, 1932). The effect of anoxia on memory has been the subject of a good deal of investigation in connexion with the problem of "pilot error". At oxygen tensions experienced at an altitude of 10,000 ft. there is a significant impairment of "immediate" memory (up to a few minutes) as indicated by objective tests: immediate memory is one of the first of the cerebral functions to suffer and the decrement is greater if the reduction in oxygen tension is rapid (McFarland, 1952).

Whatever view is taken, it seems clear that memory storage is more than one single process. At the start we have evidence of what is apparently a pattern of electrochemical activity resulting from incoming sensory stimuli. For a time this temporary record is easily displaced by agents such as anæsthetics, electrical stimulation, anoxia, concussion and even to some extent by further incoming sensory stimuli. But at some stage electrochemical events are converted into non-electrical events; and after a variable period of "consolidation" the memory trace is found to have different properties in that it is fixed in the more durable form of "long-term" memory. The shorter the time after the arrival of the sensory data, the more vulnerable is the memory trace to disturbances produced by anæsthetics and other agents and the greater the extent of the memory loss. Some forgetting occurs even in the first fraction of a second (Broadbent, 1958) and it can be shown that at this stage retention is strongly impaired by interference from other learning. Summerfield and Steinberg (1957) found that nitrous oxide gas, which is a central depressant, can *enhance* memory if given (as 30% nitrous oxide in oxygen) immediately after learning: this they attributed to the action of nitrous oxide in reducing the interfering effect of other activities on the process of retention. Certain stimulant drugs such as strychnine and picrotoxin have also been shown to facilitate learning. Strychnine is believed to increase the rate of firing of active neurons by blocking inhibitory synapses, but how it acts in facilitating learning is not yet known.

Of the numerous endocrine disorders that have been recognized, thyroid deficiency (myxœdema) is of special interest since it is commonly associated with mental changes characterized by mental slowness and loss of memory. Here the immediate memory (up to a few minutes) is relatively unimpaired: the disorder is essentially a failure of retention or consolidation with loss of memory for recent events. The thyroid hormones have been shown to act as a stimulant on protein synthesis. Their primary point of action is apparently on the genetically linked regulatory mechanisms of protein synthesis, since stimulation of the DNA-dependent RNA polymerase precedes the increased incorporation of amino acids into protein (Tata and Widnell, 1964). An indication of the kind of proteins concerned in the action of the thyroid hormones is given by the work of Eayrs (1960) who has shown that thyroid deprivation in the young animal causes a specific interference with the normal development of the dendritic tree: this suggests that the proteins induced by thyroid hormones are concerned especially with the metabolism of the dendrites.

Enzyme inhibitors The metabolic processes concerned in the various physiological functions of the brain are dependent on a number of different enzymes. By studying the effects of specific enzyme inhibitors on physiological function we can therefore hope to find out something about the metabolic processes on which the functions of the brain depend. Enzyme inhibitors known to have central actions on the brain include the anticholinesterases and the monoamine-oxidase inhibitors. These compounds do not appear to have any particular action on memory function, although the mental confusion produced by the anticholinesterase drugs is incompatible with learning. "Immediate" memory is sensitive to agents such as cyanide and carbon monoxide which act specifically on the oxidative mechanisms of the cell, but after recovery from their actions there is little or no impairment of previously established long-term memory.

Experiments designed to study the effects of metabolic inhibitors on memory were carried out by Dingman and Sporn (1961) who examined the question of whether learning depends on the synthesis of RNA. They measured the performance of rats in a swimming maze after intracisternal injection of 8-azaguanidine, which interferes with RNA synthesis, and found that it did not affect the performance in a previously learned maze but prevented the learning of a new one. However, there is evidence that 8-azaguanidine has other actions apart from inhibiting RNA synthesis, and the question was therefore reinvestigated by Barondes and Jarvik (1961) using actinomycin-D, which has been shown to inhibit the synthesis of messenger RNA in a number of bacterial and animal systems. Control experiments using the incorporation of radioactive carbon from [^{14}C]orotic acid showed that the synthesis of RNA in the mouse brain was inhibited by 83% for several hours at the dose level used, but despite this, the animals were able to learn and remember as well as controls in a simple passive avoidance conditioning situation. From these experiments it appeared unlikely that learning involves the synthesis of a unique RNA molecule concerned specifically in the function of memory.

These experiments did not exclude the possibility that learning involves the synthesis of other kinds of protein which are not dependent on a stimulus-specified RNA, for the cell normally contains other forms of RNA which can enable protein synthesis to continue for several hours after complete inhibition of the synthesis of new RNA. Flexner and his colleagues studied the effect on learning of puromycin, which does not prevent the formation of RNA but inhibits protein synthesis by blocking the action of the ribosomes. Puromycin is a relatively toxic substance, but experiments using [^{14}C]valine to measure protein synthesis showed that puromycin in a dose which inhibited protein synthesis by 83% in the mouse brain *in vivo* was not incompatible with learning or with retention of learned material. Higher doses which inhibited protein synthesis by 95% produced a state of general disorientation in which learning behaviour could not be tested reliably (Flexner *et al.*, 1962). In further experiments they found that they could inhibit protein synthesis in the brain by 80% for 8–10 hours with smaller doses which did not cause disorientation at the time of testing by injecting puromycin directly into the brain. Bilateral injections of puromycin were made into each hemisphere in three different positions at a depth of 2 mm. from the surface of the skull; fluorescein was injected in control animals to show the distribution of puromycin in the brain. With mice trained to a standard performance in a maze and injected with puromycin 1–2 days later, bilateral temporal injection caused complete loss of "short-term" memory of the training experience. By contrast, bilateral frontal, or ventricular, or combined frontal and ventricular injection were essentially without effect. In mice trained to standard performance and injected 6 or more days later, memory ("longer-term") was only destroyed by combined temporal, ventricular and frontal injections of puromycin. They concluded from these experiments that the effective locus of "short-term" memory of maze learning in the mouse spreads from the hippocampal and temporal cortex to the remaining areas of the neocortex in 3–6 days, and thereby becomes consolidated as "longer-term" memory. The time course of this spread of the memory trace was shown very clearly in experiments with reversal learning in which a second response pattern was learned some time after a first learning experience. Temporal lobe injections of puromycin removed the second pattern and restored the long-term memory for the first experience. This gave evidence that the action of puromycin was not simply that of disorganizing or incapacitating the memory mechanisms in the experimental animals. Control experiments, in which saline and various compounds chemically related to puromycin were injected instead of puromycin, gave evidence that the effect of these compounds in removing the memory of maze learning could be related to their efficacy in inhibiting protein synthesis as measured by the incorporation of [^{14}C]valine. They concluded that the maintenance of memory in the mouse depends on the continuing synthesis of protein in the brain (Flexner, Flexner and Stellar, 1963; Flexner *et al.*, 1965).

In an investigation of memory fixation in goldfish, Agranoff and Klinger (1964) found that intracranial injection of puromycin 3 days before testing was without effect on the ability to learn an avoidance response. Puromycin injected immediately after learning removed the immediate memory of the learned response: but it was without effect on a memory established over a period of several days. Measurements of [^{3}H]leucine incorporation showed that there was an 80% inhibition of protein synthesis in the brain under the conditions of their experiments.

III. Biochemical Hypotheses of Memory

Molecular coding   Chemical hypotheses of memory have been current for many years. All of these are speculative, but some are of special interest in that they have served as a basis for experimental work. The view that memory is coded at a molecular level was put forward by Monné (1948), who pointed out that antibody formation in response to the stimulus of an antigen can be regarded as a kind of learning in that the reacting cell undergoes a permanent change. He stressed the specificity of the antigen–antibody reaction and concluded that the engram is likely to depend on specific changes in the proteins of the nerve cells of the brain. Others have favoured the view that proteins are concerned in the recording of memory traces because of the large number of possible ways of changing a protein molecule (von Foerster, 1948). A more systematic attempt to develop a chemical hypothesis of memory was made by Katz and Halstead (1950) who based their views on the evidence that nucleoprotein molecules in the chromosomes act as templates from which replica protein molecules are formed. They suggested that learning involves a change in a specific nucleoprotein in the nerve cell and that this results in the synthesis of a specific "memory protein" which permanently changes the electrical properties of the cell. "In a very real sense the genetic apparatus is a memory (recapitulation) device. If, in place of endowed template molecules . . . , we postulate the formation of templates as a result of individual experience, then . . . not all of the templates are an endowment but rather some arise from external stimuli" (Halstead, 1951). Katz and Halstead postulated that an engram is established by the formation of a special protein lattice extending in the cell membrane throughout the whole neuron and even across a synapse from one neuron to another. They concluded that "each memory trace is distinguished by the chemical composition and geometrical configuration of the protein-repeating unit of its lattice".

Hydén (1959, 1962) has proposed a memory hypothesis which is also based on analogy with the genetic mechanisms of the cell as well as on the special capacity of nerve cells for synthesizing RNA and protein. He postulates the primary formation in the nerve cell of (1) a new form of RNA with a specific base sequence coded to correspond to the pattern of electrical impulses in the exciting sensory neuron. This specified RNA serves as a template for the synthesis of (2) a protein replica which is postulated to have the property of dissociating rapidly in response to the same electrical pattern of stimulation that originally specified the RNA template. The dissociation of the specific protein is assumed to liberate (3) a smaller molecule which reacts with (4) a complementary molecule already present in the cell to cause the release of (5) a transmitter substance at the synapse. It is postulated that the transmitter is released in a sequence of bursts at frequencies corresponding to the pattern of the original electrical stimulus. The modulated release of transmitter substances can thereby transmit the original stimulus pattern to a second cell. It is postulated further that each specified type of RNA continues to replicate itself indefinitely and to produce specified protein replicas in the nerve cell as long as the memory persists. The presence of the specified protein in the cell makes the cell respond differently to stimuli depending on whether an incoming pattern of impulses is a new one or a familiar one which causes the specific protein to dissociate. On this hypothesis neuronal paths grow by successive specification of the RNA molecules and the proteins formed from them. The shape of a triangle, for example, would have to be represented by a multiplicity of coded molecules in the neurons at every step in the visual system extending from the retina to multiple projection areas in the cerebral cortex.

The main evidence cited in support of the molecular hypotheses of memory storage is that the nerve cell has an active RNA and protein metabolism which cannot otherwise be accounted for. In considering this argument it is relevant that the nerve cell is also exceptional in several aspects of its amino acid metabolism (Richter, 1962, 1965; Gaitonde, Marchi and Richter, 1965). It has been shown that the brain differs from most other organs in its high content of glutamate and in

Table 1.   Incorporation of ^{14}C into the free amino acids of different organs at 22 min. after injection of [^{14}C]glucose.

	Proportion of ^{14}C in amino acids (% of total)	Specific radioactivity of amino acids (counts/min./mg. amino N)
blood	2	77
liver	9	55
kidney	14	70
muscle	12	17
cerebral cortex	70	308
cerebellum	64	286
spinal cord	72	140

Animals were injected subcutaneously with 50 μc [U-^{14}C]glucose containing 5 mg. glucose carrier in 1 ml. aqueous solution (Gaitonde, Marchi and Richter, 1964).

the way it can utilize amino acids as a source of energy. It is unique in possessing active enzymic machinery for utilizing glutamate through the GABA pathway and it is exceptional in its high rate of conversion of glucose carbon into glutamate (Table 1). The nerve cell can synthesize protein in the cell body, but it also contains a proteinase, particularly active in the axon, which is able to break down protein and liberate free amino acids (Ansell and Richter, 1954). The nerve cell has little reserve of glycogen in relation to its high metabolic activity and the evidence suggests that it is specially adapted to utilize amino acids and endogenous protein to provide the metabolites required for functional activity.

Protein synthesis is a normal function of the primitive neurosecretory cells which predominate in the nervous system of many invertebrates (Knowles, 1964); and secretory activity, which is widely found in cells of ectodermal origin, appears to persist, not only in neurosecretory cells but also in the more highly specialized types of neurons in the mammalian brain. Although protein synthesis is active in the neuron, it must be remembered that the larger neurons of the mammalian brain are the largest cells in the body and that the nerve cell body (perikaryon) provides for the requirements of dendrites and axon which are many times the size of the cell body. If it is taken that protein synthesis in the nerve cell provides reserve material, not only for the elaboration of

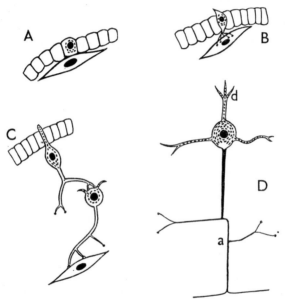

Fig. 4. Evolution of the nerve cell.
A. Epithelial cell with neurosecretory function and muscle cell, as found in the sponge.
B. Primitive nerve cell and muscle cell as in coelenterates.
C. Differentiated sensory and motor neurons as in sea anemone.
D. Vertebrate neuron with dendrites and axon.

transmitter substances, but also for the energy metabolism in maintaining the irritability of the cell membrane in dendrites and axon, the need to ascribe a special memory function to RNA and protein synthesis in the nerve cell disappears.

   Another argument advanced for the molecular hypotheses of memory is that the number of memory traces that need to be stored in the brain is very large and it is therefore likely that the vast capacity of nucleoprotein macromolecules for storing genetic information will be utilized. Some investigators have thought in terms of 10^{15} to 10^{20} items in the memory store (Hydén, 1962), but if it is taken that the brain can record

100 new items of information every second for 16 hours a day for a lifetime of 70 years, the total number of items would only be of the order of 10^{11}. It is unlikely that more than a fraction of the items recorded at this rate could be recalled, so that the number of separate memory traces needed to record a lifetime's experience might even be smaller than this. It would certainly be possible for 10^{11} items to be specified in terms of the base sequences in nucleic acid macromolecules, but the mechanism for making the coding of the base sequence correspond to the pattern of exciting electrical impulses presents serious difficulties. In a recent modification of his hypothesis, Hydén (1964) attributes the specification of the memory RNAs to pre-existing chromosomal DNA molecules. This avoids any possible conflict with Crick's "central dogma", but the essential difficulty of explaining how the coding is effected still remains. There is also the problem of accommodating the quantity of DNA required for memory coding. The number of genes in the chromosomes is commonly estimated to be of the order of 10^6 to 10^7, and if the efficiency of storage and retrieval of information from the "memory DNA" is no better than that of the genes, the amount of DNA required for storing 10^{11} specific memory items would be 1000–10,000 times that required for the recognized structural genes. For 10^{20} memory items the quantity would be formidable. A further problem is the read-out of the information stored in the 10^{11} different specified proteins. The property ascribed to them of dissociating only in response to specific stimuli would be an unusual one, as would be the property of causing the liberation of a transmitter substance in bursts at the correct frequency.

The argument that the "phylogenetic memory" of the chromosomes is similar to memory based on learning and experience is of questionable validity, for there are many points of difference between them. It is true that fairly complex behavioural patterns can be inherited and therefore can be encoded in the DNA, but the genetic mechanisms determining behaviour of this kind appear to operate by influencing the growth and structural organization of the neuronal network. An innate behavioural pattern can be triggered off by the action of an appropriate hormone, such as an androgen, but only if the underlying neuronal differentiation and cellular organization has already proceeded over a considerable period of time (Young, Goy and Phoenix, 1964). Rapid processes, such as those mediated by transmitter substances, are generally carried out by small molecules, whereas the sorting of large numbers of macromolecules must take an appreciable time. The slow "phylogenetic memory" offers no parallel to the split-second rapidity of recall of a visual image or a motor skill.

Some experiments have shown that changes occur in the quantity and average base composition of mixed RNAs in the cell bodies of neurons under conditions of stimulation and learning, but RNAs are relatively labile metabolites, and changes have been reported under a number of conditions in which learning is unlikely to be the cause. In any case changes of RNA associated with learning would not necessarily imply that memory traces are coded at a molecular level by a specific change in the base sequence of the RNA.

Other memory hypotheses   A number of memory hypotheses postulate the transfer of selected information from a temporary "short-term" store to a long-term store, involving a synaptic change. The synapses are the points of contact at which, by the release of a transmitter substance, an excitatory or inhibitory impulse can pass in one direction from one neuron to the next. The chemical transmitter substances are contained in small storage vesicles in the nerve endings, ready to be released when an electrical impulse travelling down the axon reaches the synapse. There are many possible ways in which a change at a synapse could take place. It has been thought, for example, that neuronal activity might promote the growth of the nerve endings with the formation of new synaptic connexions; or there might be a change in the lipoproteins of the synaptic membranes so that transmission is either facilitated or impaired. Clearly, changes of this kind might involve the synthesis of RNA and protein, but the change might equally well take the form of a change in quantity or distribution of a lipid constituent such as a phospholipid or sterol, which are among the more stable compounds present in the nerve cell membranes. Another possibility is that prolonged activity of a neuronal circuit might cause the amount or the nature of the transmitter substances to change. There is experimental evidence of an analogous change of this kind in the adrenal medulla, where prolonged stimulation changes the proportions of adrenaline and and noradrenaline that are released. It may also be significant that the storage vesicles in the synapses can apparently store and release compounds other than those which normally serve as transmitters: thus adrenergic nerve endings in the brain stem can apparently take up and release amines other than catecholamines. A change in the position of a synapse on the receiving neuron could also change the behaviour of a neuronal circuit, since there is a greater probability of the receiving neuron firing when the synapses are near the cell body (axosomatic) than when they are at the far end of the dendrites. There is some evidence of a general movement of the synapses towards the cell bodies as the maturation of the brain proceeds (Purpura and Shofer, 1965).

The number of possible changes affecting synaptic transmission is extended by the observation that passing a low constant current of 2–10 μamps through a small part of the motor cortex can cause an increase in excitability. This results in an apparent facilitation analogous to that which occurs in learning, so that limb movements, for example, are produced by stimuli which are normally too weak to be effective.

The increased excitability, which could be due to an ionic shift, can persist for several hours after the current has been switched off (Morrell, 1961; Bindman, Lippold and Redfearn, 1962).

Yet another possibility to be considered is that events at the synapse might be altered by distant changes affecting the electrical properties of the axons or glia. Owing to the summation of excitatory and inhibitory impulses, the effect of a train of impulses arriving at a synapse depends on the precise time at which they arrive in relation to impulses received from other branches of the neuronal network. The importance of the

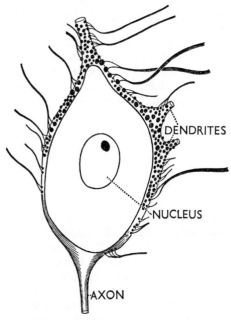

Fig. 5. Diagram of a sectioned nerve cell, showing nerve-endings forming synapses on the surface of the dendrites and cell body. The axon is free of synaptic connexions.

time of arrival of stimuli at central synapses is suggested by the observation that convulsive discharges can sometimes be evoked in epileptic subjects by photic stimulation at critical frequencies. A "resonance" phenomenon has also been observed in the dog as a result of cortical stimulation at specific frequencies. Stimulation at a point on the motor cortex at frequencies up to 17/sec. in the dog under nembutal anæsthesia causes extension of the hind leg; frequencies of 17–21/sec. cause flexion; at 21–31/sec. extension occurs again and at 34–37 flexion occurs (Foster, 1950). The time of arrival of impulses depends on the rate at which the impulses travel along the axon and the fine terminal axon filaments, in which conduction is relatively slow. It is known that the rate of conduction of an impulse depends on the diameter of the axon and also, in myelinated axons, on the properties of the myelin sheath. Hill (1950) showed that the repeated passage of impulses along an axon produced a measurable increase in diameter, which would be expected to increase the conduction rate. There is also some evidence that stimulation can influence the course of myelination. Thus myelination is generally more advanced in a 3-month old infant born prematurely at 7 months than in a one month old full-term infant, although both are 10 months from conception. Is this because the premature infant has had greater opportunities for learning? Since myelin is a product of the glial cells, the apparent effect of stimulation on myelination gives evidence of an interaction between neurons and glia, as has been indicated by other observations (Hydén, 1962). The glial reaction might be due to liberation from the stimulated neuron of a substance which induces the formation in the glial cells of enzymes required for myelin synthesis.

One of the attractions of the synaptic change hypothesis is the large amount of information that can be stored in that way. If it is taken that

(Structural gene)   DNA→mRNA→ENZYME→TRANSMITTER

(Regulator gene)   DNA ←⎯⎯⎯⎯⎯⎯⎯⎯⎯⎯⎯⎯⎯⎯⎯⎯⎯

Fig. 6. Representation of the cycle of events in which a transmitter substance induces the production of an enzyme which synthesizes it.

there are 10^{10} neurons in the human brain, each with an average of 10^3 synapses, then the total number of synapses is 10^{13} and the number of alternative patterns that can be made by an all-or-none change involving any 10 synapses will be of the order of 10^{130}. The number of patterns that could be produced by a graded modification of transmission or change of timing at any 10 synapses would be even greater. It can be seen that even if only 1% of the cells in the brain were concerned in memory storage, the possibilities for storage of information offered by the known neuronal network are extremely great.

Experiments with micro-electrodes inserted in different regions of the brain support the view that frequency modulation is utilized in the central nervous system, as in the periphery, as a method of modifying a response. In other words, facilitation of a neuronal pathway seems to imply an increase in the number of discharges per second. This could be achieved, as Briggs and Kitto (1962) have suggested, if the formation of an enzyme involved in the synthesis of a transmitter substance was induced by the transmitter itself. This would therefore be a special case of the general phenomenon of enzyme induction by substrate. The release of transmitter substance in adequate amounts from one neuron could result in the formation of transmitter in a second neuron, and a facilitated pathway could develop in this way. A mechanism of this kind would depend on the formation of a specific messenger RNA in the first place, and it would continue so long as DNA-dependent protein synthesis was maintained. The changes in RNA expected to result from stimulation might be similar to those reported in the learning experiments of Hydén, but unlike the nucleotide sequence hypothesis of memory coding, this hypothesis involves no special assumptions or biochemical mechanisms which have not already been demonstrated in other systems. Hypotheses of this kind can be extended to include changes in inhibitory substances such as GABA or in 5-HT and Substance P which can modify synaptic transmission (Roberts, 1964) and they appear to offer the simplest interpretation of the facts available at the present time.

Conclusion The brain is characterized by an active overall energy metabolism. Although the brain represents only about 3% of the total weight of the body, it accounts for one-fifth of the total heat production of the body in the normal resting state. Much of the energy requirement of the nerve cell is concerned with maintaining an irritable membrane that can be depolarized some hundreds of times a second—in other words, with working the "sodium pump". For this purpose it might seem that the brain would use energy-supplying mechanisms similar to those in muscle and other organs, which are versatile in utilizing fats as well as carbohydrates as a source of energy. But in fact we find that the brain relies almost exclusively on glucose, which it either oxidizes directly to CO_2 or converts at a relatively high rate into amino acids and proteins.

The discovery that the brain has an active protein metabolism was at first not easy to understand, for, unlike the liver or pancreas, the brain is not an organ which secretes a protein to the outside. In some respects nerve cells do resemble the cells of glandular tissues, and some nerve cells have been shown to have a neurosecretory function; but clearly the protein which is synthesized in the bodies of the nerve cells must be utilized mainly by home consumption within the brain. Part of the protein is used for the production of transmitter substances, trophic substances and enzymes such as cholinesterase, and it has been found that another part is broken down in the periphery of the cell by neutral proteinase and utilized for the energy requirements of the axon and dendrites. Protein synthesis proceeds actively whether sleeping or waking and whether learning or not. The impairment of memory in thyroid deficiency, and in the puromycin experiments, suggests that protein synthesis may come into the mechanisms of memory storage or recall; but it seems reasonable to relate the active RNA and protein metabolism of the nerve cell to the normal processes of neuronal and synaptic transmission rather than to a specific mechanism for memory coding at a molecular level. Evidence for molecular coding is in any case very slight, and present molecular hypotheses do not account satisfactorily either for the specification of RNA by electrical impulses or for the subsequent read-out of information from the hypothetical memory store.

Investigation of the memory problem by biochemical methods has revealed a number of biochemical changes which meet the first criterion of the engram, in that they are produced by the action of a stimulus on a living tissue. The second criterion, that the change must be permanent or at least durable, is more likely to be satisfied by a change in a structural lipoprotein or lipid than in a constituent as labile as RNA. But clearly the engram need not correspond to the presence or absence of any structural component of this kind: it might be represented rather by a *process* such as might result from the liberation of a self-inducing enzyme through the maturation of a pre-existing gene. The process could be as simple as the methylation of a hydroxyl group so long as it influences neuronal transmission. The number of different possibilities is immense.

Whatever its chemical nature may be, a memory trace can be produced, and ultimately demonstrated, only through patterns of electrochemical activity entering or emitted from systems of cells linked by synapses. It would seem then that in looking for the engram a chemical change at a synapse is the first possibility to be explored. There are many different ways in which a synaptic pathway might be facilitated or modified, and a number of hypotheses have been proposed; but no hypothesis can be wholly satisfactory that does not also take into account the *motivational* aspect of memory in the living animal. Psychologists have recognized for many years that the memory store is not simply a magnetic tape device for the passive recording and retrieval of information. More than 99% of the sensory information continually reaching the brain is quickly forgotten. The small fraction ($< 1\%$) selected for retention is not passively recorded, but grasped as an active process by the living organism because of its apparent relevance to the basic drives, for possible use at some future date (Rapaport, 1942). This means that memory is in fact a compound of *two* sets of information, one sensory and one motivational, depending on appetites, drives and the autonomous activity of the living brain. The information selected for memory storage in man may be more limited in range of sensory data than in some humbler species: it is hard, for example, for us to conceive of the experiential quality of the different planes of polarized light which are meaningful to the bee. But the higher animals show a wider range of variation in motivational cues: one may have a specially developed memory for mating calls, another for stocks and shares.

It is easier at the present time to frame biochemical hypotheses of the engram than to devise satisfactory experiments for testing them, and a major problem is that of knowing where to look for the effective change in the brain. The cruder memory hypotheses involving an all-or-none effect localized at a single neuron or synapse are no longer tenable. Studies with implanted electrodes suggest that even the simplest mental activity involves some millions of neurons. In Lashley's (1942) experiments, the removal of large sections of the cerebral cortex failed to reveal any sharp localization of one type of memory in the mammalian cortex. Yet it is believed that memory is localized to some extent in special lobes in the brains of simpler animals such as the octopus (Young, 1964) and there is evidence that the special kinds of visual and auditory memory are associated to some extent with the corresponding sensory projection areas in the mammalian cortex. A subcortical localization has been suggested for associative learning and some localization of function is also apparent in the limbic system and hypothalamus which, as main controlling centres of autonomic activity and affective behaviour, might be thought to mediate the motivational component of memory. From a biochemical viewpoint it may be significant that regions displaying metabolic differences are becoming more clearly defined. Cholinergic and adrenergic transmission are not uniformly distributed throughout the brain, but localized to some extent in special regions. It would appear that the prospects of finding out more about the engram will be improved when more is known about the general biochemistry and the localization of biochemical function in the brain.

References

Agranoff, W. and Klinger, P. D. (1964), *Science*, **146**, 952.
Ansell, G. B. and Richter, D. (1954), *Biochim. biophys. Acta*, **13**, 92.
Barondes, S. H. and Jarvik, M. E. (1961), *J. Neurochem.*, **11**, 187.
Bennett, E. L., Diamond, Marion C., Krech, D. and Rosenzweig, M. R. (1964), *Science*, **146**, 610.
Beringer, K. (1932), *Nervenarzt*, **5**, 346.
Bertram, E. G. and Barr, M. L. (1949), *Anat. Rec.*, **103**, 567.
Bindman, L. J., Lippold, O. C. J. and Redfearn, J. W. T. (1962), *Nature, Lond.*, **196**, 584.
Brattgård, S. O. (1952), *Acta radiol.* Suppl. 96, 1.
Brierley, J. B. (1966), In *Aspects of Learning and Memory*, p. 25 (Edited by D. Richter), Heinemann, London.
Briggs, M. H. and Kitto, G. B. (1962), *Psychol. Rev.*, **69**, 537.
Broadbent, D. E. (1958), *Perception and Communication*, Pergamon Press, Oxford.
Chentsov, I. S., Boroviagin, V. L. and Brodskii, V. I. (1961), *Biophysics*, **6**, 61.
Chitre, V. S., Chopra, S. P. and Talwar, G. P. (1964), *J. Neurochem.*, **11**, 439.
Clouet, D. E. and Richter, D. (1958), *J. Neurochem.*, **3**, 152.
Cohen, M. M. (1962), *J. Neurochem.*, **9**, 337.
Cohn, P., Gaitonde, M. K. and Richter, D. (1954), In *Structure and Function of the Cerebral Cortex*, p. 340 (Edited by D. B. Tower and J. P. Schadé), Elsevier, Amsterdam.
Cook, L., Davidson, A. B., Davis, D. J., Green, H. and Fellows, E. J. (1963), *Science*, **141**, 268.
Dawson, R. M. C. and Richter, D. (1950a), *Amer. J. Physiol.*, **160**, 203.
Dawson, R. M. C. and Richter, D. (1950b), *Proc. roy. Soc. B*, **137**, 253.

Dingman, W. and Sporn, M. B. (1961), *J. Psychiat. Res.*, **1**, 1.
Dingman, W., Sporn, M. B. and Davies, R. K. (1959), *J. Neurochem.*, **4**, 154.
Dolley, D. H. (1913), *J. med. Res.*, **29**, 65.
Eayrs, J. T. (1960), *Brit. med. Bull.*, **16**, 122.
Eccles, J. C. and McIntyre, A. K. (1951), *Nature, Lond.*, **167**, 466.
Edström, J. E. (1964a), *J. Neurochem.*, **11**, 309.
Edström, J. E. (1964b), *J. Neurochem.*, **11**, 557.
Edström, J. E. and Grampp, W. (1965), *J. Neurochem.*, **12**, 735.
Edström, J. E., Eichner, D. and Edström, A. (1962), *Biochim. biophys. Acta*, **61**, 178.
Fischer, R., Zeman, W. and Irons, I. (1961), *J. Histochem. Cytochem.*, **9**, 103.
Flexner, J. B., Flexner, L. B., de la Haba, G. and Roberts, R. B. (1965), *J. Neurochem.*, **12**, 535.
Flexner, J. B., Flexner, L. B. and Stellar, E. (1963), *Science*, **141**, 57.
Flexner, J. B., Flexner, L. B., Stellar, E., de la Haba, G. and Roberts, R. B. (1962), *J. Neurochem.*, **9**, 595.
Foerster, H. von (1948), *Das Gedächtnis*, Vienna.
Foster, A. A. (1950), *Fed. Proc.*, **9**, 41.
Freundl, G., Gerlach, J. and Turba, F. (1964), *Biochem. Z.*, **341**, 9.
Gaitonde, M. K., Marchi, S. A. and Richter, D. (1964), *Proc. roy. Soc. B*, **160**, 124.
Gaitonde, M. K. and Richter, D. (1953), *Biochem. J.*, **55**, 8.
Gaitonde, M. K. and Richter, D. (1956), *Proc. roy. Soc. B*, **145**, 83.
Geiger, A., Yamasaki, S. and Lyons, R. (1956), *Amer. J. Physiol.*, **184**, 239.
Grampp, W. and Edström, J. E. (1963), *J. Neurochem.*, **10**, 725.
Grande, F. and Richter, D. (1950), *J. Physiol., Lond.*, **111**, 57P.
Gutmann, E. (1964), *Prog. Brain Res.*, **13**, 72.
Halstead, W. C. (1951), In *Cerebral Mechanisms in Behaviour* (The Hinxon Symposium), p. 244 (Edited by L. A. Jeffress), Chapman & Hall, London.
Hamberger, C. A. and Hydén, H. (1949), *Acta oto-laryng.*, **53** (Suppl. 75), 82.
Heald, P. J. (1959), *Biochem. J.*, **73**, 132.
Hebb, C. and Silver, A. (1965). *XIII Annual Colloquium on Protides of Biological Fluids*, Brugge.
Hill, D. K. (1950), *J. Physiol., Lond.*, **111**, 304.
Himwich, W. A., Dravid, A. and Berk, T. (1965), In *Amines and Mental Illness* (Atlantic City Symposium), (Edited by H. E. Himwich), Pergamon Press, Oxford.
Hydén, H. (1943), *Acta physiol. Sèand.*, **6** (Suppl. 17), 88.
Hydén, H. (1959), In *IVth Int. Congr. Biochem. Vienna*, Vol. III, p. 64, Pergamon Press, Oxford.
Hydén, H. (1962), In *Macromolecular Specificity and Biological Memory*, p. 55 (Edited by F. O. Schmitt), M.I.T. press, Cambridge, Mass.
Hydén, H. (1964), *Neurosciences Research Program Bull.* II, No. 3, 23.
Hydén, H. and Egyházi, E. (1962), *Proc. nat. Acad. Sci., Wash.*, **48**, 1366.
Hydén, H. and Egyházi, E. (1963), *Proc. nat. Acad. Sci., Wash.*, **49**, 618.
Hydén, H. and Egyházi, E. (1964), *Proc. nat. Acad. Sci., Wash.*, **52**, 1030.
Hydén, H. and Lange, P. (1965), *Proc. nat. Acad. Sci., Wash.*, **53**, 946.
Hydén, H. and Pigon, A. (1960), *J. Neurochem.*, **6**, 57.
Jakoubek, B. and Edström, J. E. (1965), *J. Neurochem.* **12**, 845.
Jakoubek, B., Gutmann, E., Hajek, I. and Syrovy, I. (1963), *Physiol. Bohemslov.*, **12**, 553.
Jasper, H., Khan, R. T. and Elliott, K. A. C. (1965), *Science*, **147**, 1448.
Katz, J. J. and Halstead, W. C. (1950), *Comp. Psychol. Monogr.* **20**, 1.
Knowles, F. (1964), In *Comparative Neurochemistry*, p. 3 (Edited by D. Richter), Pergamon Press, Oxford.
Köcher, R. A. (1916), *J. comp. Neurol.* **26**, 341.
Lajtha, A. C., Furst, S., Gerstein, A. and Waelsch, H. (1957), *J. Neurochem.*, **1**, 289.
Larrabee, M. G. and Leicht, W. S. (1965), *J. Neurochem.*, **12**, 1.
Lashley, K. S. (1942), *Biol. Symp.* Vol. VII, 301.
Liu, C. N., Bailey, H. L. and Windle, W. F. (1950), *J. comp. Neurol.*, **92**, 169.
MacIntosh, F. C. and Oborin, P. E. (1953), *Abstr. XIX Int. Physiol. Congr.*, p. 580.
McFarland, R. A. (1952), In *The Biology of Mental Health and Disease*, p. 335 (Edited by S. Cobb), Cassel, London.
Miani, N. (1963), *J. Neurochem.*, **10**, 859.

Monné, L. (1948). *Advanc. Enzymol.*, **8**, 1.
Morrell, F. (1961), *Physiol. Rev.*, **41**, 443.
Morrell, F. (1962), In *Macromolecular Specificity and Biological Memory*, p. 73 (Edited by F. O. Schmitt), M.I.T. press, Cambridge, Mass.
Palladin, A. V. (1957), In *Metabolism of the Nervous System*, p. 456 (Edited by D. Richter), Pergamon Press, Oxford.
Purpura, D. P. and Shofer, R. J. (1965), In *Regional Maturation of the Nervous System in Early Life* (Edited by A. Minkowski), Blackwell, Oxford.
Rajalakshmi, R., Govindarajan, K. R. and Ramakrishnan, C. V. (1965), *J. Neurochem.*, **12**, 261.
Rapaport, D. (1942), *Emotions and Memory*, Williams & Wilkins, Baltimore.
Richter, D. (1962), *Res. Publ. Ass. nerv. ment. Dis.*, **40**, 268.
Richter, D. (1965), *Brit. med. Bull.*, **21**, 76.
Richter, D. and Crossland, J. (1949), *Amer. J. Physiol.*, **159**, 247.
Richter, D. and Dawson, R. M. C. (1948), *J. biol. Chem.*, **176**, 1199.
Ridge, J. (1961), *Biochem. J.*, **78**, 280.
Roberts, E. (1964), In *Learning, Remembering and Forgetting* (Edited by D. Kimble), Science and Behaviour Books, New York.
Samuels, A. J., Boyarsky, L. L., Gerard, R. W., Libet, B. and Brust, B. (1951), *Amer. J. Physiol.*, **164**, 1.
Shapot, J. S. (1957), In *Metabolism of the Nervous System*, p. 257 (Edited by D. Richter), Pergamon Press, Oxford.
Sikdar, K. and Ghosh, J. J. (1964), *J. Neurochem.*, **11**, 545.
Summerfield, A. and Steinberg, H. (1957), *Quart J. exp. Psychol.*, **9**, 146.
Talwar, G. P. and Chitre, V. S. (1965), Personal communication.
Tata, J. R. and Widnell, C. C. (1964), *Biochem. J.*, **92**, 26P.
Ungar, G. and Romano, D. V. (1962), *J. gen. Physiol.*, **46**, 267.
Vladimirov, G. E. (1953), *Fiziol. Zh. (Mosk.)*, **39**, 3.
Vrba, R. and Folbergrova, J. (1959), *J. Neurochem.*, **4**, 338.
Warren, K. S. and Schenker, S. (1960), *Amer. J. Physiol.*, **199**, 1105.
Weiss, P. and Taylor, A. C. (1965), *Science*, **148**, 669.
Young, J. Z. (1964), *A Model of the Brain*, Clarendon Press, Oxford.
Young, W. C., Goy, R. W. and Phoenix, C. H. (1964), *Science*, **143**, 212.

Electrical Signals in the Brain and the Cellular Mechanism of Learning

B. S. Meldrum

No attempt will be made in this chapter to review the very considerable literature reporting and speculating on correlations observed between electrical events in the brain and learning, partly because several reviews cover this field in greater detail than would be possible here (Morrell, 1961; Galambos and Morgan, 1960; John, 1961). Besides, it is not yet possible to differentiate between those changes in cerebral electrical activity occurring during conditioning procedures which play an essential part in the formation of the memory trace, or engram, and those which are secondary to some otherwise irrelevant feature of the experimental situation. An example of the latter is the blocking of the α-rhythm which occurs as part of the "orienting response". This replacement of the rhythmic 8–12 cyc./sec. electrical activity of the occipital cortex in the relaxed subject by irregular low-voltage fast activity when a novel stimulus is presented does not necessarily form a link in the production of the engram. This is shown, for example, by the ready establishment of conditioning in the presence of drugs which prevent this blocking of the α-rhythm. The changes that take place in the rhythmical electrical activity in different parts of the brain during conditioning experiments are summarized by John (1961).

A view of the problem of the physiological substrate of learning that emphasizes the role of the synapse will be developed and some rather individual speculations about the mechanisms involved will be advanced. It is felt that the present lack of direct evidence of what happens at the cellular level in learning should not deter us from discussing what these mechanisms might be.

I. Outline of the Problem

The synapse and input–output relationships of the nervous system We shall assume that "learning" refers to changes in response patterns, or behaviour, that are consequent to specific experiences. Changes in behaviour that automatically accompany maturation or sexual cycles, regardless of experience, come into the category of "instinctive behaviour". We have much detailed information about the afferent sensory messages, or input, to the brain, and nearly as much about the output or efferent system (motor and secretory nerves). To explain what happens in the brain during learning we must show how broadly similar inputs can lead to very dissimilar outputs as a result of learning.

The input Behavioural responses to the environment must be mediated via the sensory input to the nervous system. In man this arises principally from the receptor neurons in specialized sense organs (the eye and ear) but also from dispersed receptors such as those for touch in the skin and for tension in the muscle tendons. It is transmitted by a large number of sensory fibres (perhaps six million) to the central nervous system. The signal in each fibre is in the form of a brief change in the electrical potential across the nerve cell membrane, lasting about one thousandth of a second. This change or "action potential" propagates itself at a speed ranging from 0·5 to 120 m./sec. according to the diameter of the fibre. Such an impulse can be followed by another one in the same fibre within about two milliseconds. Three things define the message that such impulses carry: (1) the specific channel or nerve fibre that it is travelling in; (2) the gap in time between it and the preceding and the following impulses in the same channel; and (3) its relation to the overall pattern in space and time of the impulses in the other channels converging with it at the afferent relay stations.

Analysis and integration of the messages occur whenever one nerve fibre terminates in synaptic contact with another. This arises since the relationship of the presynaptic terminal to the postsynaptic cell is not simply one-to-one (with rare exceptions such as the ciliary ganglion and some synapses in the central auditory pathway). The number of fibres leaving a relay station is not necessarily the same as the number arriving there. One primary afferent fibre may terminate on many second-order cells, and one second-order cell may receive synaptic contacts from many primary afferent fibres. Initiation of an impulse in the second nerve cell in the input sequence will usually require activity in more than one of the fibres ending presynaptically on it. A single impulse can initiate a postsynaptic impulse if the other presynaptic fibres are providing the necessary background activation. In view of the large number of presynaptic channels that can relay on to a second-order cell and the possibility of inhibitory as well as excitatory postsynaptic actions, and the long period (up to 100 msec.) over which such inputs may interact, complex transformations of the message can occur at each relay stage. The number of such synaptic relays that the message passes on its way from the primary receptor neuron to the cells in the appropriate specific sensory area of the cortex is between two and five, varying according to the sensory modality.

For several sensory modalities the kinds of transformation that occur at each relay have been determined in animal experiments by using microelectrodes to record impulses in single fibres on either side of the relay while accurately defined sensory stimuli are being applied. This has been done in the visual pathway (Hubel and Wiesel, 1959, 1961, 1962), in the auditory pathway (Ades, 1959; Whitfield, 1955) and in the somatosensory system (with joint position sense by Mountcastle, Poggio and Werner, 1964; with skin pressure receptors by Armett *et al.*, 1962).

In the visual system at the level of the optic nerve fibres (which come from the retinal ganglion cells) the message in any single fibre relates to the increase or decrease of illumination in two concentric circular discs in the retinal field. At the lateral geniculate nucleus, onto whose cells the optic nerve fibres relay, the receptive fields for the single cells remain circular, but the overall illumination is less significant; it is the contrast between the centre and the periphery of the field that is more important. The response patterns of the cells in the visual cortex have also been examined. The information here has been transformed so that it relates to the movement of boundaries of light and dark across the retina. As the information is further processed within the cortex it becomes highly specific as to the extent of the light–dark boundary and its direction and speed of movement.

The kind of processing of information in any one afferent pathway remains constant. Modifications in transmission at any of the synaptic levels can be produced by efferent impulses coming from the cortex, but this appears to be primarily a resetting of the gain rather than a change in the type of information processing. Such modifications may be involved in attention and habituation mechanisms but it is unlikely that they are important for learning.

Not all the sensory input travels via the specific sensory pathways. Some goes directly to reflex centres in the spinal cord or brain stem and influences the motor output after one or more synapses. Other inputs activate neurons in a "non-specific" afferent system which includes the reticular formation. This is a diffuse structure in the brain stem in which single cells responding to a variety of auditory, visual or somatic stimuli are found. Activity here is transmitted either up through median thalamic structures to the association areas of the cortex and the limbic system, or down to efferent centres in the spinal cord. Activity in this non-specific sensory system can modify the overall pattern of oscillation in electrical potential recorded at the cerebral cortex. It is assumed to be involved in the process by which the cortex isolates and "attends" to significant stimuli.

There is another completely different type of input to the nervous system which is of considerable significance in learning. This is the input provided by the blood. Metabolically important alterations in the blood such as changes in glucose content, oxygen or carbon dioxide tension and temperature cause changes in cell-firing rates in the hypothalamus (Cross and Silver, 1963). Cells in this region of the brain also show variations in activity according to the concentration of steroid hormones (e.g. œstrogen and progesterone) in the blood.

The output Like the input, the major part of the output of the brain is coded as impulses in nerve fibres. These travel, either via the cranial nerves or spinal cord to the muscles producing bodily movement and speech, or via the autonomic nervous system to influence secretory processes and visceral movement.

There are several relay systems whereby the motoneuron that activates the "voluntary" muscle fibres is influenced by the tension in the muscle tendon, by the tone of other muscles acting on the same joint and neighbouring joints, and through the muscle spindles. The latter comprise very fine muscle cells with their own motor supply, enclosed with various sensory endings in a narrow capsule. They provide a feedback loop for the fine control of muscle tension.

The interactions of factors affecting the motor nerve cell have been thoroughly explored—initially by the study of reflexes under the leadership of Sherrington and more recently by the study of the inter-action of inhibitory and excitatory postsynaptic potentials in single cells in the cat spinal cord (Eccles, 1964). As in the case of information transfer and integration on the input side, the synaptic and action potentials convey the whole story, and the pattern of interaction that they display appears to be rigidly determined.

The output carried in the autonomic nervous system acts on the "involuntary" muscles of the viscera, blood vessels and heart and on those organs whose secretory function is under nervous control (including some of the endocrine glands). The actions of this system produce many of the bodily changes associated with biologically significant (or "emotionally charged") experiences. These bodily changes may in turn provide a secondary sensory input to the nervous system. Such mechanisms operate in many learning situations.

One output of the nervous system is not coded in terms of nerve impulses. This is the neurosecretory function of the hypothalamus and the posterior part of the pituitary gland. Cells in nuclei in the hypothalamus synthesize peptide hormones which are transported in bound form to the terminations of these neurosecretory cells in the pituitary gland. When nerve impulses originating in the cell bodies in the hypothalamus reach these terminals, the hormone is released into the blood stream.

Synaptic links between input and output   The structure and spatial arrangement of the nervous elements "connecting" the specific sensory areas and the motor system is known in moderate detail (Ramón y Cajal, 1911). However, the functional properties of these "connexions" remain problematical. Although the gross electrical behaviour of the various parts of the central nervous system has been studied, how this behaviour relates to the processing of information by the constituent single cells is not known. Light and electron microscopy have shown that nerve cells in the brain make contact with one another in many different ways, both in terms of the parts of the cell involved ("axo-dendritic", "axosomatic", "axo-axonal", etc.) and in terms of the specialized structures within the presynaptic knobs and the spacing and thickness of the presynaptic and postsynaptic membranes. Broadly the appearances suggest that these synapses operate in a way similar to those on the afferent and efferent pathways, that is, presynaptic impulses release chemical transmitters which produce postsynaptic potential changes which excite or inhibit postsynaptic impulses. Intracellular electrical recordings from cortical cells do indeed indicate that just the same kinds of integration of excitatory and inhibitory postsynaptic potentials occur here as in the motoneurons of the spinal cord. The inhibitory potentials in cortical neurons apparently have a longer time course than in spinal neurons (Phillips, 1961).

Now comes an admission of ignorance. It is not certain that all the transformation of input to output is achieved by the mechanism of action and synaptic potentials, or that the specialized synaptic structures are the only means by which one cell passes messages to others. The big question-marks relate to the functions of the special cellular features of the brain (in particular the cerebral cortex)—the dendrites and the glia.

The dendrites   These are the diffuse branches of neurons which in the cortex may extend for 1 mm. in more than one direction from the cell body and may contact as many as 1000 other cells. One doubt about their function in terms of strict synaptic theory arises because pre-synaptic action on the extremity of a dendrite seems unlikely to be able to influence electrical events at the cell body where the axon originates. This and several types of experimental observation have led to speculation that dendritic structures are specializations for producing, and responding to, direct current field potentials.

The glia   These small cells are packed between the nerve cells and apparently play a nutritive and supportive role. They do not themselves transmit electrical signals, but there are several ways in which they might produce slow sustained effects on the excitability of adjacent nerve cells. The simplest way would be by changing the ionic composition (particularly the concentration of sodium, potassium and calcium) of the fluid bathing the nerve cell membrane. A more probable mechanism is by changing the concentrations of glutamic acid and γ-aminobutyric acid or related amino acids at the nerve cell membrane. These substances excite (glutamic acid) or inhibit (γ-aminobutyric acid) nerve cells quite generally. Their distribution in subcellular fractions (Whittaker, 1965) suggests that they are unlikely to be the chemical agents for "conventional" synaptic transmission in the cerebral cortex. They are actively metabolized by cerebral tissues and their concentration in the brain and the rate at which they diffuse out from its surface varies with its state of activity (Jasper, Khan and Elliott, 1965). Glial cells, by altering the rate of synthesis, release, or uptake of these amino acids, may produce long-lasting effects on nerve cell activity.

A biochemically more complex hypothesis is that glial cells influence nerve cells by the synthesis and exchange of ribonucleic acid (see pp. 73–99).

In summary, in an animal responding to its environment, (1) the output of its nervous system is governed by the input; (2) the mechanism by which information is transformed from the input to the output side includes signals which are nerve cell action and synaptic potentials; (3) the transformation that occurs is determined by the pattern of connexions between the nerve cells, the integrative properties of the synapses, and the pre-existing pattern of activity in the system. In some circumstances the pre-existing pattern of activity may influence the output to the extent that it appears not to be dependent on the input ("spontaneous behaviour").

The nascent engram, the mature engram, and the recall file We have considered broadly how the cellular elements in the nervous system operate and we shall now review some simple observations that have a direct bearing on the relationship between learning, brain cell activity and the patterns of connexions between the cells. Because of the vast number of active units in the brain, it is clear that the pattern at any one instant is never exactly repeated. Since the overall pattern of activity in the brain at the moment a novel stimulus occurs will influence the subsequent output, we may ask whether sustained patterns of electrical activity could be the essential substrate of learning.

Hypothermia Experiments on hypothermia (e.g. Andjus *et al.*, 1956; Mrosovsky, 1963) show that self-maintaining patterns of excitation within the nervous system are not the explanation for the persistence of learned responses. In a typical experiment of this kind, rats which had learned a conditioned avoidance response during a 20-min. training period were rested for 15 min., then anæsthetized and cooled until their body temperature fell to 1°C. After resuscitation there was no significant loss of retention compared with control animals not exposed to low temperatures. Gross "electrical silence" of the brain occurs when the body temperature falls to 18°C. Although nerve cells can conduct impulses at 1°C, it is certain that integrated nervous activity cannot sustain itself at this temperature, Nor is it likely that the pattern of activity could reform during resuscitation in a way precisely determined by its previous activity, because the different groups of nerve cells would resume their biochemical and electrical functions at different rates thus disrupting the latent pattern. We are led to the conclusion that a structural change, presumably at the synaptic level, underlies learned responses.

Fragility of the nascent engram   Many traumata encountered in clinical medicine or experimental psychology severely disrupt the pattern of cerebral nervous activity. These include anoxia, profound anæsthesia, mechanical disturbance (concussion) and epileptic seizures either occurring spontaneously or induced by drugs or electroconvulsive shock. Once consciousness has been regained following such traumata it can be shown that responses acquired at any time up to a brief period before the trauma are retained. The precise duration of the period of impaired retention varies not only with the species of animal and the type of trauma but also with the type of response that is being tested. In general, however, the impairment of retention is most severe if the trauma comes within 1–2 min. of the learning situation and is decreasingly severe over the following 30 min. or so. If the disruption of cerebral activity occurs one hour or more after the training it causes no loss of retention in rats.

The period of vulnerability of the nascent engram to electroshock can be extended by cooling the animal after the training. This suggests (but does not prove, since changes in nerve conduction velocity may be involved) that metabolic energy is required for "consolidation" or the establishment of the mature engram. This and the fact that disruption of the electrical activity of the brain impairs consolidation does not necessarily mean that consolidation depends on a long-sustained pattern of electrical activity, such as reverberatory circuits or slow potential fields. All that is known to be required for the formation of the engram is time and ordered activity. Slow processes involving neurosecretion or protein synthesis might equally well constitute the vulnerable stage before the mature engram is established.

The recall file   After certain traumata there may be a period during which responses learned at various times beforehand are lost, but subsequently these responses return. This occurs in humans after concussion (see pp. 13–24) and can be shown in animals given electroconvulsive shock. In such cases a stable or structural change has occurred, but, apparently the access system to this change (the "recall file") has been temporarily blocked.

Speaking of the "nascent engram", the "mature engram" and the "recall file" is merely a shorthand way of referring to the experimental observations mentioned above and is not intended to indicate anything about the physical nature of the changes involved.

Correlating this and the previous section we may say that the establishment of the mature engram takes time, depends on ordered nervous activity, and involves a change in the functional pattern of synaptic connexions within the nervous system.

Innate patterns of synaptic connexions and coding on RNA   A brief look at how the pattern of synaptic connexions comes into existence initially is appropriate before we discuss how it might be changed.

Experiments have established that many complex patterns of behaviour seen in adult mammals are truly innate. This applies, for example, to nest-building behaviour displayed by rats reared in isolation in restricted environments (Eibl-Eibesfeldt, 1961). These innate patterns of behaviour are readily integrated with learned responses.

Clearly, complex patterns of synaptic connexions can be coded in a form that is genetically transmissible. Presumably the information is coded on DNA in the gametes and later transferred to RNA. Given that the pattern of synaptic connectivity required for innate behaviour can be coded on RNA then at first sight it might seem to be a valuable simplification to suggest that the modified synaptic connexions required for learning are coded on RNA. But this is not a helpful hypothesis. Firstly there is no mechanism known whereby the information can be coded on to the RNA. Secondly the read-out of the genetic information from the RNA (i.e. its decoding into a pattern of synaptic connexions) is a process that takes more than a year in man. In this time structural proteins, enzymes and chemical inducers (whose structures are determined by the RNA) initiate processes whose subsequent interactions evolve through all the stages of the embryo to yield the nervous structure of the infant. The synthesis of one molecule of protein using the RNA template takes about 20 sec., but the "read-out" involved in the execution of a complex learned task takes less than one-tenth of a second.

The only known way in which information coded on RNA could contribute to the read-out underlying a learned response is if it determined the pattern of synaptic connexions. But there is no evidence that such a record exists for learned responses. Provided that synaptic connexions are permanent and only undergo modification during learning, then there is no need for the hypothesis that acquired synaptic patterns are coded on RNA.

Of course RNA is inevitably involved in the formation and maintenance of the engram, if only because protein synthesis is required.

Changes in RNA are therefore to be expected during learning; but this is not to say that learned information is coded on RNA.

The simplest assumption is that the pattern of synaptic connexions as established by primary growth processes or by previous learning remains constant except when new learning occurs.

II. Synaptic Plasticity—Some Sparse Evidence

Such direct evidence as exists concerning the occurrence of functional changes at the synaptic level will now be examined.

The presumed occurrence of changes in synaptic transmission following use or disuse played a critical role in several theories of learning now largely overlooked (e.g. Hebb, 1949). The basic postulates were that (a) prolonged use of a synapse leads to a sustained facilitation of transmission across it and (b) a significant sensory input initiates a self re-exciting pattern of activity (in a "reverberatory circuit") and this leads to the permanent memory trace by the mechanism specified in (a). Such theories ignored the structural profusion and functional complexity of synapses and do not fit in well with our knowledge of synaptic changes following use or disuse as studied directly at peripheral neuro-effector junctions and in spinal cord reflexes and, indirectly, in the brain.

Peripheral neuroeffector junctions   It is established that lack of activity at a peripheral nerve terminal (on skeletal muscle, smooth muscle or gland cells) leads to an enhancement of transmission or increased responsiveness of the effector cell. Some manifestations of this phenomenon have been grouped together under the heading of "denervation supersensitivity". The diminished activity may be produced in a wide variety of ways including cutting the nerve itself or cutting the more central nerves which activate it (e.g. preganglionic sympathetic fibres) or preventing the synthesis or release of the chemical transmitter by drug treatment.

Whichever procedure is used the increased responsiveness develops over a period of one to two weeks and varies in intensity according to the severity of deprivation. The effector cell becomes more responsive to its specific transmitter but may show enhanced responsiveness to substances which normally have only slight effects. Thus denervated skeletal muscle contracts in response to noradrenaline.

This enhanced responsiveness is not due to slower destruction of transmitter but to either an increase in the number of receptor sites or some other change in the postsynaptic cell membrane (Miledi, 1962). In denervated skeletal muscle the area of muscle cell membrane that responds to locally applied acetylcholine increases enormously.

This phenomenon of increased sensitivity following a sustained period of diminished or absent activation seems to be universal for all peripheral neuro-effector junctions. Detailed descriptions occur in reviews by Trendelenburg (1963) and Sharpless (1964).

The spinal cord   Among spinal reflexes those concerned with the maintenance of posture may be expected to show stability of function rather than plasticity. Spinal reflexes related to noxious stimuli, however, manifest decreasing responsiveness with repetitive activation ("habituation"). Although this habituation is normally mediated by descending influences from higher centres including the cortical association areas, sustained effects can be produced in animals with transection of the cervical spinal cord provided the repetitions are maintained over a long period. In such a "spinal" kitten, loss of a withdrawal reflex can be produced after two weeks training. There is no direct information about the synaptic changes in habituation.

Changes in responsiveness with use and disuse have been studied at the synaptic level (see Eccles, 1961). The simplest change is "post-tetanic potentiation". Enhancement of a monosynaptic reflex lasting for 1–2 min. is produced by repetitive activation of the reflex at a high frequency (e.g. 400/sec.) for several seconds. This is probably produced by hyperpolarization of the presynaptic terminal which leads to a greater release of transmitter by the presynaptic nerve impulse.

Effects of disuse on monosynaptic reflexes have been studied in cats by cutting the dorsal roots distal to the ganglion on one side. Six weeks later a comparison of the response to dorsal root stimulation on control and operated sides showed severe impairment of transmission on the operated side. This impaired pathway exhibits post-tetanic potentiation which is greatly enhanced both in relative amplitude and in duration.

Effects of excessive use of monosynaptic pathways can be tested by cutting the tendons of all except one of a group of synergistic limb muscles of the cat, exercising the animal, and then comparing monosynaptic responses for the over-exercised muscle and the control muscle on the other side. In this way a 50% increase in the monosynaptic reflex can be shown to follow several weeks of excessive use.

These experiments on use and disuse of spinal monosynaptic reflexes do not greatly advance our understanding of the synaptic changes in learning. The results of experiments on disuse appear contrary to the findings in the periphery and perhaps in the brain, and are complicated by the occurrence of degenerative changes in the presynaptic terminals. Decay with disuse would be a mixed blessing in many accounts of learning mechanisms as the maintenance of learned responses over long periods in which no overt practice occurs has then to be accounted for in terms of "spontaneous activity" providing concealed practice. The time course of the observed effects of use and disuse bears no relation to that of engram formation, but this discrepancy is not surprising as rapid learning is not displayed by the spinal cord.

Experiments on functional regeneration after surgical transpositions of peripheral nerves and muscles provide information about the power of regression for inappropriate synapses and of regeneration of previously established pathways. That the capacity to regenerate and reform synaptic connexions in a precisely determined way is highly developed in fishes and amphibians has been shown by the work of Weiss (1952) and Sperry (1950). Sperry (1947) was unable to demonstrate comparable synaptic reorganizations in the spinal cord connexions in rats and monkeys. However, Eccles *et al.* (1962) by cross-uniting hind-limb nerves in kittens and six months later recording reflex responses in spinal cord cells, found some slight but significant evidence that motoneurons whose axons after regeneration supplied a changed muscle did acquire some new monosynaptic afferents. Such new synaptic connexions do not in any sense represent "learning" but are examples of regeneration where some chemical specification of the motoneuron ensures the appropriateness of its afferent synaptic connexions. The evidence for the formation of regenerated or new synaptic connexions in the mammalian nervous system is very limited. McCouch *et al.* (1958) have suggested on the basis of electrophysiological and histological studies in animals with chronic spinal transections, that the limb spasticity these animals display is associated with sprouting and proliferation of the spinal afferent terminals, so that they occupy parts of the motoneuron surface made available through the degeneration of long descending nerve tracts. This capacity for new growth displayed by dorsal root fibres may not be shared by central neurons in general.

The ability of central neurons to form synaptic connexions after injury does not necessarily have any bearing on the reorganization of synaptic connexions postulated by learning theories. However, the relative lack of ability of the mature mammalian nervous system to regenerate must make us cautious about the possibility of new synapses growing in the course of learning.

The brain   Out of the wide variety of procedures that can produce changes in the excitability or the functional synaptic patterns of the cerebral cortex, two which provide parallels with learning will be described.

"Mirror-image" epileptic foci   A primary epileptic focus, produced by local cortical damage, can lead to the development of a secondary focus in a corresponding location on the opposite cortex (see Morrell, 1961). In the rabbit this can occur within about 24 hours. Initially this focus is dependent on the primary one in that it displays paroxysmal activity only in parallel with the primary focus and, if the primary focus is removed, its activity returns to normal. After about a week it becomes independent and will persist if the primary focus is excised. Preliminary transection of the corpus callosum prevents the formation

of a mirror-image focus. If a mirror-image focus is cut off from any input by converting it to an isolated cortical slab it becomes electrically silent but its excitability remains abnormally high. Morrell has suggested that such foci provide an important model of learning and that excessive activity transmitted by callosal fibres is here producing enhanced excitability which, since it persists after de-afferentation, must depend on structural changes at the cellular level.

However, other mechanisms may be involved both in establishing and in maintaining a mirror-image focus. Cortical undercutting experiments, which show that abnormal callosal input cannot by itself set up a focus, suggest that thalamo-cortical interactions are important. The persistence of abnormal excitability after cortical isolation is complicated by the fact that changes in excitability normally accompany this procedure. Chronically isolated cortical slabs (with blood supply intact but with all nervous connexions cut) have an enhanced sensitivity to locally applied acetylcholine and they show much more prolonged after-discharges than freshly isolated slabs. There may be a parallel here with peripheral denervation supersensitivity. In agreement with this view, loss of callosal afferents can cause normal cortex to become more excitable. In the kitten isolated cortical slabs show a proliferation of recurrent collaterals arising from the severed axons (Purpura, 1961). In summary, the sustained alteration in excitability shown in mirror-image epileptic foci is a complex phenomenon and the mechanism at the cellular level is obscure.

Cortical polarization Another procedure which modifies cortical responsiveness and is possibly related to mechanisms operative during learning is the application of small direct currents to the cortex. Rusinov (see reviews by Rusinov and Rabinovich, 1958; Morrell, 1961; O'Leary and Goldring, 1964) observed that anodal polarization of the motor cortex in rabbits modified the animal's responsiveness to auditory or visual stimuli. During passage of the current, limb movements determined by the position of the polarizing electrode were found to follow previously ineffective sensory stimuli. Motor responses thus linked to sensory inputs during current flow could still be induced by the same sensory inputs for up to half an hour after the current had ceased. Rusinov and Morrell speak of the current flow inducing temporary links between sensory and motor areas. Other long-lasting effects of cortical polarization have been reported by many authors. Morrell thinks it significant that the duration of these after-effects is similar to that of the vulnerability of the engram to disruption by electroshock.

The cellular mechanism by which polarizing currents modify excitability is not known. Polarizing currents applied to peripheral synapses or spinal cord dorsal roots probably affect the amount of transmitter released. Changes in acetylcholine content and cholinesterase activity in the cortex under polarizing electrodes have been reported. Other possible causes of prolonged after-effects are re-distribution of electrolytes or amino acids, or changes in neuronal or glial membrane permeabilities, these effects arising either as direct consequences of current flow or being secondary to changes in cell activity. Burns (1954) showed that surface-positive polarization increased the firing rate of cortical cells, and the persistence of this effect after cessation of current flow has been described by Bindman, Lippold and Redfearn (1964).

Interest in the effect of DC currents on cortical activity is enhanced by the fact that shifts in the surface potential of the cortex have been observed in the course of conditioning experiments. Rowland and Goldstone (1963) recorded shifts in surface potential of the cat cortex following the presentation of conditioned stimuli that were reinforced 10 sec. later with food. Grey Walter *et al.* (1964) have recorded negative shifts in potential that occur diffusely over the human cortex between the presentation of a warning stimulus and the performance of a response. It is unlikely that these potential shifts are related to the embedding of the engram. They probably arise from activity in non-specific afferent systems.

Enriched experience   There is some evidence linking cortical growth with the complexity of experience. Bennett *et al.* (1964) kept weanling or adult rats in "enriched" and "simple" environments. Comparing littermates they found an increase in the weight and thickness of the cortex and an increase in the total acetylcholinesterase activity, in direct association with the complexity of experience. There is also evidence (Altman and Das, 1964) that an enriched environment can increase the rate of multiplication of glial cells. Studies in animals and man of the growth of interconnexions between cortical cells have suggested that such growth precedes or runs parallel with the capacity to learn, rather than that learning can induce dendritic growth in the cortex. However, no explicit test of this had been attempted prior to the "enriched environment" experiments, but even here the operation of mechanisms totally unrelated to learning, may be producing the cortical growth.

III. Synaptic Plasticity—Some Speculations

Hypothetical synaptic modifications   In the seventy years that have passed since Ramón y Cajal suggested that learning is accompanied by the formation of new synaptic connexions between the cells in the cortex, regrettably little evidence for such changes has been found. Great progress has been made in understanding the links between the release of chemical transmitter substances, changes in cell membrane permeability to specific anions and cations, and nerve cell impulse generation. This knowledge can help us in formulating hypotheses about mechanisms of synaptic change. Three kinds of change may be considered: growth of new synaptic connexions; loss of synaptic connexions; and changes in the effectiveness of pre-existing synapses.

Growth of new synapses As mentioned previously, the evidence that during the course of maturation in the mammalian nervous system the regenerative capacity of its neurons declines whereas its overall learning capacity increases argues against, but does not exclude, the possibility that learning depends on the formation of new synaptic connexions. There is, however, no direct evidence that new synapses are formed in the intact adult brain in relation to any learned responses. It is difficult to envisage a system for regulating such growth that could specify both the growing and receptive cells.

Loss of synaptic connexions This is a more attractive hypothesis for several reasons. Firstly, it is well established that synapses are lost throughout adult life. Certain histological staining procedures reveal degenerating synapses sparsely scattered in the normal brain. Cortical cell counts on brains of different ages have established that many thousands of cells degenerate during each day of adult life. Secondly, inhibition or interruption of one of two alternative pathways is the simplest system to utilize when designing models of the reorganization of nervous pathways during learning. This kind of mechanism fits very well with the overall reciprocal pattern employed by the nervous system in every aspect of its output to effector organs. We can imagine that a rewarded response leads to sustained inactivation of either inhibitory connexions to the effector neurons that initiated the response or of excitatory connexions to their antagonists. In either case the likelihood of this response being repeated under similar circumstances will be increased. A punished response will lead to sustained inactivation of either the excitatory afferents to the responsible effector neurons or the inhibitors of their antagonists. A model of this kind has been proposed by Young (1964, 1965) to account for learning in the octopus, and parallel features have been observed between the model and the histological organization of the octopus nervous system.

Could all learning be accounted for by the blocking-off or loss of synaptic connexions? The initial synaptic connexions, determined partly by random growth, must, in the possible alternatives that they represent, "contain" all possible learned responses. This apparent paradox is not a serious difficulty, but the possibility that successive periods of learning could so reduce the number of available synaptic pathways as to impair further learning might be. As such impairment is not seen in practice, a second postulate that neighbouring terminals will proliferate to fill gaps left by blocked-off or degenerating terminals (as apparently happens below a spinal cord transection) seems to be called for. Postulating a growth of new synapses that is only secondary to the loss of others overcomes the problem of how the brain specifies new connexions.

Modifications of existing synapses   We shall ignore here any possible role of the glial cells.

Some biochemically-oriented learning theorists favour changes in the concentration of enzymes synthesizing or destroying transmitter substances as the basis of learning. This provides a control mechanism employing RNA. However, normal function in cholinergic synapses where these factors have been assessed is not influenced by increasing the rate of synthesis or destruction of acetylcholine, and decreasing either rate produces effects on transmission which vary with the rate of stimulation. In fact it looks a most unsatisfactory regulatory system.

Other, perhaps more probable, mechanisms are a change in the structure of the presynaptic terminal so that the transmitter released is either greater in quantity or more effective, or a change in the post-synaptic receptor field of the sort seen with use and disuse at peripheral junctions.

Perhaps the most attractive hypothesis is that synaptic terminals migrate along dendrites, moving nearer to the cell body to enhance their function, and towards the dendrite tip to diminish it. This hypothesis has the advantage of assigning a function to the synapses on the distant parts of dendrites which, on electrophysiological grounds, are thought to be incapable of influencing the initiation of impulses in the axon. Their role would be to keep a register of cells that could develop functional contacts.

Venom polypeptides that act on synapses   The question naturally arises as to whether there are any chemical agents known that could be the mediators of (1) synaptic blockade and destruction, and (2) dendritic growth permitting the migration of existing synapses or the formation of new synapses. Among known compounds those most nearly fitting these requirements are found in high concentration in snake and insect venoms. These venoms contain many pharmacologically active agents including several low-molecular weight compounds known or believed to be chemical transmitters in the mammalian or invertebrate nervous system (including acetylcholine, urocanylcholine, histamine, dopamine, 5-hydroxytryptamine, homarine, octopamine, tetramine and various kinins).

The venom constituents that may be significant for learning are the nerve growth factor and the polypeptide toxins. The nerve growth factor (see Levi-Montalcini, 1964) is a protein known to occur in snake venoms, in the mouse salivary gland and in the immature nervous system. It greatly enhances the growth of sympathetic and sensory nerve cells in tissue culture or in the developing animal, but has not yet been shown to promote the growth of nerve cells in the brain.

The polypeptide toxins (see Meldrum, 1965) found in the venom of snakes such as cobras and kraits have diverse physical properties but their actions on peripheral synapses fall precisely into two groups. Either, in the course of a few minutes, they enter into an irreversible combination with components of the postsynaptic membrane, including perhaps the receptors for acetylcholine thus preventing the muscle from responding to stimulation by its nerve; or over a period of 30–60 min. they destroy the ability of the presynaptic terminal to release acetylcholine.

If the polypeptide toxins are, like the other non-enzymic constituents of snake and bee venoms, related to nervous transmitter substances, then apparently the only role that they could play is in the production of long-lasting changes in synaptic function. They are not inhibitory transmitters but can block transmission which might itself be either excitatory or inhibitory.

Although a protein similar to venom nerve-growth factor has been found in the nervous system, polypeptides with long-lasting effects on synaptic transmission have not so far been identified in the nervous system. One polypeptide that has been purified from brain tissue is Substance P. This, in low concentrations, affects the contraction of smooth muscle. Zetler (1960) found that the injection of crude Substance P produced definite effects on brain activity, such as sedation, potentiation of barbiturates, antagonism to convulsant drugs, and antagonism to the depressant effects of morphine. However, pure preparations of Substance P have been shown not to have these actions (Vogler *et al.*, 1963). This difference between crude and pure Substance P is probably due to the presence in the crude preparation of other polypeptides which can act on synaptic transmission (Zetler, 1963).

A mechanism for engram formation which utilizes polypeptides with sustained effects on synapses would permit a very simple control system—nerve impulses in specific pathways causing the release or neurosecretion of the polypeptide leading to block of the appropriate synapse. The inhibition (by puromycin or similar agents) of protein and polypeptide synthesis in regions of the brain normally responsible for the elaboration of these "learning transmitter-substances" would prevent the acquisition of new responses.

If factors promoting nerve growth play a part in learning, their local release need not necessarily be under nervous control. They could be released as a secondary consequence of the degeneration of synapses in accordance with the suggestions made above (p. 113).

The mature engram, the unit of learning and cortical localization For any particular learned response, where in the brain do the synaptic changes occur? There are overwhelming reasons for believing that in humans the majority of the changes occur in the cerebral cortex. A simple consideration of the "unit" of a learned response indicates that changes must occur in many parts of the cortex. Thus in human experiments if a telephone number is taken as a unit of learning, evidence of retention can be evoked by auditory or visual inputs and demonstrated by outputs which may involve speech or limb movements.

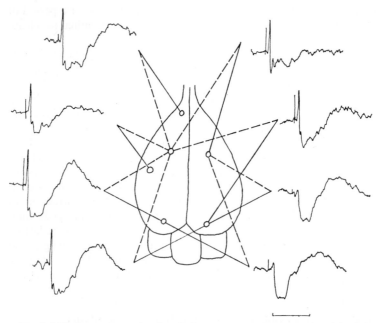

Fig. 1. This figure shows the electrical responses to shocks to the right forepaw in the unanæsthetized rabbit, recorded with implanted epidural silver-silver chloride electrodes. Each trace is the average of 60 consecutive responses recorded between the electrode placements indicated. Time calibration: 100 msec.

An early positive wave with a peak latency of 8–10 msec. is seen at the contra-lateral somatosensory cortex. A later negative shift occurs in both cerebral hemi-spheres. (I am grateful to Devices Sales Ltd. for the loan for 76 hours of an Enhance-tron 1024 digital computor.)

The appropriate synaptic changes cannot be restricted to one sensory or motor area of the cortex.

The multiple and diffuse cortical representation of learned responses was demonstrated in the classical studies of Lashley (1950). In one series of experiments rats were trained in mazes or in visual discrimina-tion and were tested for retention after removal of specific cortical areas. The impairment produced was related to the total volume of cortex removed rather than to the specific region. This apparent diffu-

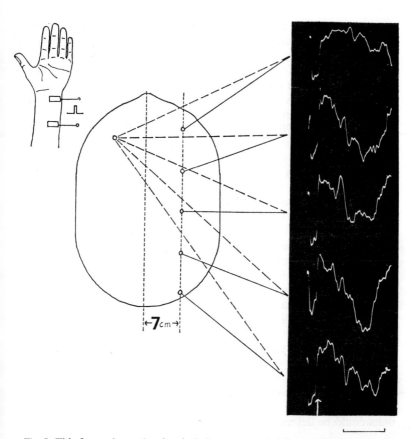

Fig. 2. This figure shows the electrical changes recorded from scalp electrodes in the conscious human subject in response to shocks to the left wrist. Each trace is the average of 50 consecutive responses at 2-sec. intervals, and begins with a 2 μV calibration pulse. The stimulus, given at the end of the voltage calibration, is indicated by the arrow. Time calibration: 50 msec.

An early positive-negative-positive complex, occurring 15–25 msec. after the stimulus, is most prominent in the contralateral somatosensory region. A subsequent positive shift with a latency of 35–40 msec. is seen more widely in the cortex. (Note that bilaterally symmetrical events in the frontal cortex will not be demonstrated with the electrode placement used here). The author acknowledges the collaboration of I. B. Gartside and O. C. J. Lippold in this experiment.

sion or dissemination of the engram has now been demonstrated in many ways including the experiments involving section of the corpus callosum (see pp. 150–153). Such dissemination of the engram does not strengthen the case for a chemical coding of the engram. It is merely what current electrophysiological findings lead us to expect if the coding is by changes in synaptic patterns.

Two different procedures can be used to show that any sensory input alters the electrical activity in many parts of the cortex. The averaging procedures introduced by Dawson (1954) permit the gross electrical changes that follow a specific stimulus to be added algebraically with many repetitions of the stimulus. Responses that follow a stimulus in any modality within one-third of a second can be recorded over many regions of the cortex (see Figs. 1 and 2). The other procedure for demonstrating the widespread effects of any sensory input was devised by Burns and Smith (1962). They recorded impulses from single cells in the unanæsthetized cat cortex and found that all the units displayed some "spontaneous" activity. By plotting the probability of an impulse occurring at various intervals within 1 sec. of a particular stimulus it was shown that the firing of nearly every cell (large enough to permit recording) in the cerebral cortex can be influenced by a sensory stimulus in any modality or by an electrical stimulus to any other part of the cortex.

Every time a stimulus is received and a learned response made, most of the cells of the brain are involved. Learning theorists were misled by analogies with telephone circuitry and theories involving fixed conditioned-reflex pathways. A changed net output when many cells of the brain are involved can be produced in two ways; either by a multitude of exceedingly small changes in synaptic efficiency or by a smaller number of major changes (i.e. total loss of specific synapses and the formation of new synapses). If learned responses depend on a large number of minimal synaptic changes then the difficulty of identifying the changes will be increased. But the synaptic unit as seen by the electron microscope (i.e. the presynaptic terminal) is already a small unit in relation to a whole cell and total loss or replacement of such units could be detected by procedures already available.

IV. Future Research

What should be the strategy for future research?

Learning in the mammalian nervous system is a more complex process than this chapter indicates. It involves simultaneous activity in many anatomical subdivisions of the brain. We can not yet say which parts are analysing the input, which parts are holding a record of the immediate past input and output to permit correlation with the consequences, which parts are determining the sites where synaptic changes must be made in order to achieve a particular modified response and which parts are ordering the changes to be made. However, many clues are available on these points and combined electrophysiological, psychological and neuropathological studies are likely to provide the answers (or perhaps show us that these are the wrong questions).

But the changes at the cellular level may be more elusive. Direct approaches are not impossible. The formation of new synapses might be detected by the incorporation of radioactive isotopes during learning procedures and their subsequent detection by autoradiography.

Our knowledge of the very transient electrical changes at synapses has grown fast but there has been no comparable increase in our understanding of their general biological properties. This is also true of the dendritic structures and of the glial cells. Wherever learning is found in the animal kingdom, there also are found glia and dendrites, but their properties that may relate to learning are unknown.

Probably it is premature to attempt studies of learning at the cellular level until we know much more about the basic properties of the units involved.

Possibly it is premature even to discuss them.

References

Ades, H. W. (1959), In *Neurophysiology*, Vol. I, p. 585, American Physiological Society, Washington.

Altman, J. and Das, G. D. (1964), *Nature, Lond.*, **204**, 1161.

Andjus, R. K., Knopfelmacher, F., Russell, R. W. and Smith, A. U. (1956), *Quart. J. exp. Psychol.*, **8**, 15.

Armett, C. J., Gray, J. A. B., Hunsberger, R. W. and Lal, S. (1962), *J. Physiol., Lond.*, **164**, 395.

Bennett, E. L., Diamond, M. C., Krech, D. and Rosenzweig, M. R. (1964), *Science*, **146**, 610.

Bindman, L. J., Lippold, O. C. J. and Redfearn, J. W. T. (1964), *J. Physiol., Lond.*, **172**, 369.

Burns, B. D. (1954), *J. Physiol., Lond.*, **125**, 427.

Burns, B. D. and Smith, G. K. (1962), *J. Physiol., Lond.*, **164**, 238.

Cross, B. A. and Silver, I. A. (1963), *Exp. Neurol.*, **7**, 375.

Dawson, G. D. (1954), *Electroenceph. clin. Neurophysiol.*, **6**, 65.

Eccles, J. C. (1961), In *Brain Mechanisms and Learning*, p. 335, Blackwell, Oxford.

Eccles, J. C. (1964), *Physiology of Synapses*, Springer, Berlin.

Eccles, J. C., Eccles, R. M., Shealy, C. N. and Willis, W. D. (1962), *J. Neurophysiol.*, **25**, 559.

Eibl-Eibesfeldt, I. (1961), In *Brain Mechanisms and Learning*, p. 53, Blackwell, Oxford.

Galambos, R. and Morgan, C. T. (1960), In *Neurophysiology*, Vol. III, p. 1471, American Physiological Society, Washington.

Hebb, D. O. (1949), *The Organization of Behaviour*, Wiley, New York.

Hubel, D. H. and Wiesel, T. N. (1961), *J. Physiol., Lond.*, **155**, 385.

Hubel, D. H. and Wiesel, T. N. (1962), *J. Physiol., Lond.*, **160**, 106.

Jasper, H. H., Khan, R. T. and Elliott, K. A. C. (1965), *Science*, **147**, 1448.

John, E. R. (1961), *Ann. Rev. Physiol.*, **22**, 451.

Lashley, K. S. (1950), In *Physiological Mechanisms in Animal Behaviour*, p. 454, Cambridge University Press, London.

Levi-Montalcini, R. (1964), *Ann. N.Y. Acad. Sci.*, **118**, 149.

McCouch, G. P., Austin, G. M., Liu, C. N. and Liu, C. Y. (1958), *J. Neurophysiol.*, **21**, 205.

Meldrum, B. S. (1965), *Pharmacol. Rev.* (In press).

Miledi, R. (1962), In *Enzymes and Drug Action* (Ciba Symp.), p. 220, Churchill, London.

Mrosovsky, N. (1963), *J. comp. physiol. Psychol.*, **56**, 811.

Morrell, F. (1961), *Physiol. Rev.*, **41**, 443.

Mountcastle, V. B., Poggio, G. F. and Werner, G. (1964), In *Information Processing in the Nervous System*, p. 196, Excerpta Medica, Amsterdam.

O'Leary, J. L. and Goldring, S. (1964), *Physiol. Rev.*, **44**, 91.

Phillips, C. G. (1961), In *The Nature of Sleep (Ciba Symp.)*, p. 4 (Edited by G. E. W. Wolstenholme and M. O'Connor), Churchill, London.

Purpura, D. P. (1961), *Ann. N.Y. Acad. Sci.*, **94**, 604.

Ramón y Cajal, S. (1911), *Histologie du Système Nerveux de l'Homme et des Vertébrés*, Maloine, Paris.

Rowland, V. and Goldstone, M. (1963), *Electroenceph. clin. Neurophysiol.*, **15**, 474.

Rusinov, V. S. and Rabinovich, M. Y. (1958), *Electroenceph. clin. Neurophysiol.*, Suppl. 8.

Sharpless, S. K. (1964), *Ann. Rev. Physiol.*, **26**, 357.

Sperry, R. E. (1947), *Arch. Neurol. Psychiat., Chicago*, **58**, 452.

Sperry, R. W. (1950), *J. comp. Neurol.*, **93**, 277.

Trendelenburg, U. (1963), *Pharmacol. Rev.*, **15**, 225.

Vogler, K., Haefely, W., Hurlimann, A., Studer, R. D., Lergier, W., Strässle, R. and Berneis, K. H. (1963), *Ann. N.Y. Acad. Sci.*, **104**, 378.

Walter, W. G., Cooper, R., Aldridge, V. J., McCallum, W. C. and Winter, A. L. (1964), *Nature, Lond.*, **203**, 380.

Weiss, P. (1952), In *Patterns of Organization in the Central Nervous System*, p. 3, Williams & Wilkins, Baltimore.

Whitfield, I. C. (1955), *Electroenceph. clin. Neurophysiol.*, **7**, 153.

Whittaker, V. P. (1965), *Progr. Biophys.*, **15**, 39.

Young, J. Z. (1964), *A Model of the Brain*, Clarendon Press, Oxford.

Young, J. Z. (1965), *Proc. Roy. Soc. B*, Croonian Lecture, 1965 (In press).

Zetler, G. (1960), In *Polypeptides which Affect Smooth Muscles and Blood Vessels*, p. 179, Pergamon Press, Oxford.

Zetler, G. (1963), *Ann. N.Y. Acad. Sci.*, **104**, 416.

Animal Learning and Memory

I. Steele Russell

I. Information Storage

Physical systems and biological systems can have as a common characteristic the property of information storage. In its broadest sense, memory refers to the processes by which the effects of experience are preserved and later revealed in behavioural terms. For the engineer the concept of memory is quite specific; it refers to the place in the computing machine where data or information is stored. In neurophysiological terms the memory trace or engram refers to the physical record of previous events.

Viewing memory in these terms it is clear that information storage is an essential prerequisite for a change in behaviour through learning. If the salient characteristic of learning is the modification of behaviour through experience, then this can be achieved only by means of memory storage. In fact the phenomena of memory and learning are inseparable: memory without learning is no more feasible than is learning without memory. It must be emphasized that from an experimental point of view investigations of possible memory mechanisms can be undertaken only in terms of the effects of learning on behaviour. One must study memory in terms of the retention of what has been learned.

Complexity of changes involved in learning   When an animal learns, its reactions to a given stimulus, or stimulus situation, are modified. Sensory activity, whatever its form in the nervous system before learning, leads to a changed output after learning has occurred. The conclusion that a change of some kind has occurred in the neural network mediating the relevant nerve impulses would appear to be axiomatic. Clearly this statement in no way specifies the nature of the change or necessarily regards each learned response in terms of new connexions on a cerebral switch-board. This was very much the approach of Pavlov (1928), who came to view the establishment of a conditioned reflex in terms of "the closure of a circuit" between a conditioned and an unconditioned cortical analyser. Subcortical structures were regarded as being merely relay stations for either sensory inputs or motor output signals going respectively to and from cortical analysers. The formation of sensory response connexions fundamental to conditioning was conceived of in terms of pathways (cortico-cortical) in the cortex. There has been a great deal of speculation concerning the possible nature of these cortical stimulus–response (S–R) connexions in terms of possible low resistance pathways being established in the network of interneurons between the input cells (sensory analyser) and the output cells (motor analyser).

Such changes may occur during learning, but they certainly do not exist in any simple or discrete fashion in the cortex. The removal of various areas of the human cerebral cortex by the neurosurgeon has never led to reports of specific memory loss. Indeed Hebb and Penfield (1940) indicate that even very extensive removal of cortex in humans produces little measurable loss either in terms of memory or intelligence. It is only in cases involving bilateral lesions of the parieto-temporal cortex that memory losses are occasioned. Furthermore, Lashley (1929b, 1950) has shown that the removal of specific areas of cortex does not affect habits selectively. The loss of prior maze learning was found to be dependent upon the size of lesion and independent of its site in the cortex. Clearly the memory trace in the brain must be diffuse, operating as a functional unit and not localized as an anatomical entity. It must involve neurons distributed all over the cortex.

Learning as a processing of neural data   Considerations so far, concerning the possible neurological representation of learning, have been limited by implicit assumptions about the nature of the information storage involved. For a more accurate comprehension of the nature of learning, it must be borne in mind that learning does not necessarily refer to a unitary process. This is an issue which unfortunately has never been completely resolved (Skinner, 1937; Hilgard and Marquis, 1940; Konorski, 1948; Spence, 1956): but the weight of evidence seems to be in favour of at least two different types of learning, as exemplified on the one hand by Pavlovian conditioning and on the other by contingency learning, which means "learning what to do" in any task situation. This issue is basic to the degree of success that can be expected from investigations of mechanisms of learning. Perhaps it is not unfair to say that one of the most serious difficulties in this regard is the limitation imposed on research endeavours by the basic uncertainty of the nature of the phenomena that are to be explained. One cannot wait until psychological research has clarified this problem: one must simply make the most of the facts that are available.

From this point of view it would seem advantageous to regard learning and memory within the broader context of the processing of sensory information by the brain. This approach was implicit in Ashby's view (1954), and has recently been formally developed at length by Young (1964). If the brain is considered as a complex homeostatic machine, the function of sensory data processing would be to maintain a stable state. The notion that learning and memory are a type of data sorting implies that at least three distinct phases are involved—encoding, storage, and retrieval of information.

The encoding phase of learning has been characterized in terms of the fact that information has first to be registered in the nervous system before a record can be made. It is commonly accepted that during this encoding phase a certain fixation time, which may be of the order of half an hour, is required for the information to become consolidated and hence permanently stored. What has not been stressed is that this phase of learning is more than a simple registration period. It is during this phase that a great deal of sensory filtering and ordering of information occurs, either simultaneously with or before its registration in the brain. During encoding, information is "analysed" according to the manner in which it is selectively received in the central nervous system. The type of sensory data sorting by the brain determines the kind of learning that occurs. Several types of such data processing can be distinguished in terms of differing types of learning.

The most elementary type of data analysis would be the rejection of certain stimuli as being irrelevant to behaviour and therefore superfluous or redundant in that context. Examples of this are the processes of habituation and scanning. A second type of sensory processing is the correlational analysis that is involved in the formation of stimulus associations. A third type of processing is the analysis of the consequences of different types of response (contingency analysis of stimulus–response relations): this forms the basis of learning what to do in any situation. These different types of sensory processing may have different encoding mechanisms as well as different storage sites.

Once information has been stored in the brain, it must be available to be able to affect behaviour. The retrieval of information from storage can involve either direct recall or recognition. There can be a failure in retrieval without any storage loss: thus an animal which shows no retention of learning in terms of recall or recognition, may show significant retention in terms of savings in relearning.

It is clear that memory involves a complex sequence of data-processing operations and entails far more than just a storage of information. In studying the neural mechanisms of memory storage, consideration must be given to the related processes of encoding and retrieval. It is entirely possible that different "memory" systems exist in terms of the various types of data processing that underlie different forms of learning. Furthermore, any learning involving complex discriminations and choices probably represents a behavioural aggregate of more than one form of conditioning. The failure to have considered these possibilities may well account for some of the difficulties encountered in the past.

II. Redundancy Learning

One of the central problems in learning concerns the manner in which the brain can integrate the relevant sensory information. The main question is the way in which the central nervous system distinguishes between the relevant and the irrelevant from the complex of sensory information at its disposal. It would seem on *a priori* grounds that the most necessary analysis during the encoding of learning is the rejection of irrelevant stimuli, i.e. sensory inputs that are useless in the sense that they are non-informative are simply excluded from subsequent data processing. This redundancy analysis could be achieved by either habituation, or in terms of shifts of attention or sensory scanning. Redundancy learning is a term used here to describe a process which involves the rejection or disregarding of irrelevant material.

Habituation   Habituation or attentive or investigatory responses occur when stimuli are both stereotyped and repetitive. The habituated animal learns to cease reacting to such stimuli. The ignoring of the ticking of the clock or the adjustment of an animal to the novel aspects of a testing apparatus are examples of this behaviour. Sokolov (1960) has pointed out that habituation always involves an orienting reflex. Pavlov (1928) introduced the term orienting reflex to refer to the diffuse pattern of responses produced by any stimulus change, independent of its sensory modality. Such a response is perhaps the basis of sensory scanning or attention. It is characterized by a wide range of such reactions as eye movements, changes in respiration, body movements, or change in the position of the body. Autonomic changes also occur in the form of alterations in heart rate, galvanic skin response, and vascular responses. Finally, a lowering of sensory thresholds is also found accompanied by desynchronization of the electroencephalogram (EEG). Such a generalized orienting reflex is produced by any novel arousing stimulus. With repetition, stimulus habituation of the orienting reflex gradually takes place. The generalized orienting response disappears in 10–15 trials, leaving only orienting responses specific to the input modality. Habituation of these specific orienting reflexes takes place after 30 to 40 trials.

Sokolov (1960) indicated that the initial generalized nature of the orienting reflex can serve to increase the discriminatory power of other sensory systems, e.g. arousal by sound augments electroretinogram responses to flicker stimulation. Similar results have been found by Fuster (1957) for visual discrimination in monkeys. Brief electrical

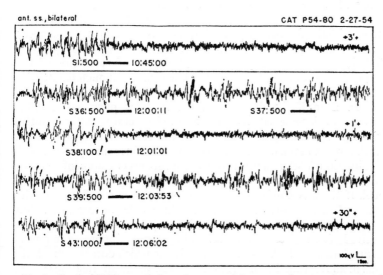

Fig. 1. Cortical EEG records from the suprasylvian gyrus of a normal cat, showing typical habituation of the arousal reaction to a 500 cycle tone after about 30 trials. In the first record the response to the first presentation to the 500 cycle tone is shown (S1 : 500). The solid bar shows the duration of the stimulus followed by the time in hours, minutes and seconds (10 : 45 : 00). In the second tracing is shown the 36th and 37th trials (S36 and S37). Then a novel tone (!) of 100 cycles is given on the 38th trial (S38 : 100!) followed by a repetition of the habituated tone (S39 : 500) and then another novel tone (S43 : 1000!). The figures at the right above the EEG traces indicate the duration of the activation in each trial (Sharpless and Jasper, 1956).

stimulation of the mesencephalic reticular formation was found to improve the level of visual discrimination. Lindsley (1958) found that two light flashes spaced closely enough to one another would produce a single large evoked response in the lateral geniculate body. With the stimulation of the brain-stem reticular formation, the evoked response separates into two peaks. Similar modulation by the reticular formation of single units in the lateral geniculate has been reported by Suzuki and Taira (1961). Clearly the reticular formation plays an important role in the facilitatory effect of the generalized orienting reflex.

With repetition of the stimulus, habituation seems to develop through feedback control of the input of the non-specific brain-stem system to the rest of the brain. This is seen in the study of electroencephalogram arousal reaction by Sharpless and Jasper (1956). As can be seen in Fig. 1, prolonged EEG desynchronization followed the initial presentation of a 500 cyc./sec. tone. With subsequent presentations the duration of this orienting response was reduced until, by trial 37, there was no response whatsoever. This response decrement is not due to fatigue since presentation of a 100 cyc./sec. tone immediately elicits a return of the orienting response. Ellingson (1958) has shown, in human infants, habituation of cortical evoked responses to regularly repeated flashes of light. With change of light frequency, evoked responses were seen to reappear. Similar observations have been reported by John and Killam (1959).

Sokolov (1960) has investigated the degree of specificity of this learning not to respond. From his work it seems as though habituation is remarkably specific to all the main parameters of the redundant stimulus. Even if the duration of the stimulus presented is either shortened or lengthened, the orienting reflex returns at the point of deviation. It is this precise nature of the selective exclusion of the orienting reflex that led Sokolov to formulate a filter theory as the basis of habituation. With repetitive stimulation, some cells store information about the modality, intensity, and duration of the stimulus as a neural model. If there is conformity between the parameters of the stimulus input and the model, then habituation would be complete. Any discrepancy would produce the orienting response. Habituation is thus conceived of as a selective and precise filtering out of orienting responses to redundant stimuli. A novel stimulus is one which does not match the model in all respects. From this point of view of the information storage that is involved in habituation, it is important to note that habituation to a stimulus of border-line threshold value cannot be obtained. This would suggest that under conditions of inadequate information, it is not possible to store information of the parameters of the stimulus.

Sokolov (1960) views habituation as being dependent not only on the formation of a neuronal model but also on the development of an inhibitory state. A schematic representation of this hypothetical orienting mechanism is presented in Fig. 2. Here it can be seen that afferent stimuli can reach either the cortical storage system or an amplifying system conceived of as the reticular formation. Whenever any aspect of an input stimulus fails to match that of the cortical model, an orienting reflex is produced. This discordance generates a cortico-fugal discharge to the reticular formation to produce orienting. When the input matches the model, there is no corticofugal arousal of the reticular formation. With repetition there is an actual cortical inhibition of the reticular formation, blocking collateral afferent input to the brain-stem and producing habituation. The main advantage of Sokolov's hypothetical system lies in his formulation of habituation as a type of selective filtering involving inhibition as well as information storage.

By means of chronically implanted electrodes, it has been possible to monitor the changes in brain activity during habituation. With electrodes in the dorsal cochlear nucleus, Galambos (1956) and Hernandez-Peon and Scherrer (1955) have recorded changes in electrical potentials during acoustic habituation of non-anæsthetized cats. Responses to a click presented every 2–3 sec. initially, resulted in large evoked responses throughout the neuraxis over and above the auditory pathways involved

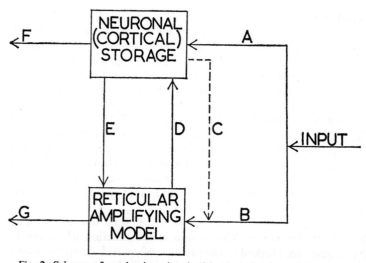

Fig. 2. Scheme of mechanisms involved in the orienting reflex. The functional connexions are: A. specific pathways from the receptor to the storage system; B. collateral afferent paths to the reticular system; C. inhibitory feedback from cortical neuronal model to the afferent reticular pathways; D. ascending reticular activating pathways to cortex; E. cortico-reticular connexions indicating accordance or discordance between stored model and afferent input; F. corticofugal pathways for specific responses; G. reticulofugal pathways for nonspecific somatic and visceral responses. Adapted from Sokolov (1960).

(Galambos, 1958; John and Killam, 1959; Jouvet and Hernandez-Peon, 1957; Morrell, Naquet and Gastaut, 1957; Yoshii *et al.*, 1960).

With repeated presentation of the click, changes like habituation are indicated by the progressive reduction in amplitude of the evoked responses and their disappearance from all areas of the brain other than the sensory nuclei. During this decremental period, wide fluctuations in amplitude occur before the cessation of response in the lemniscal pathways (Galambos, 1958; Gershuni *et al.*, 1960; Hernandez-Peon, 1960; John and Killam, 1959; Roitbak, 1960). Similar observations on the course of habituation in the visual system to light flashes have been reported by Hernandez-Peon (1960). With habituatory presentation of the light flashes over long periods, the evoked responses at each point along the visual pathways tended to diminish in amplitude.

After habituation has been attained, if the click is then associated with a shock to the foreleg or across the chest, a high amplitude cochlear response will reappear. Subsequently, habituation can be restored by a return to the constant presentation of the click. The reduction of evoked responses throughout the development of habituation along with the phenomenon of *dehabituation* suggest the role of inhibitory mechanisms mediating this exclusion of sensory input.

Attentional shifts   A redundancy analysis is mediated by habituation only where information, that ceases to be significant in a particular situation, is monotonously and repetitively presented. If this were the sole method of excluding irrelevant information, then learning would be a tedious process requiring prolonged trial and error. Indeed one of the main characteristics of learning is the fact that it is not a gradual incremental process but that, typically, sudden and rapid gains are made (Estes, 1960). Such "insight" behaviour (Köhler, 1925) is characterized by sudden changes in the pattern of responding. From a period of relatively unsuccessful trial and error, there is an abrupt resolution of the problem as if the animal had suddenly responded to the correct stimulus features of the situation. Such changes in attention suggest the existence of a type of system that enables sudden and rapid changes in the scanning of sensory information.

The distracting effect of attentional shifts was termed *external inhibition* by Pavlov (1928). This is seen in the situation where conditioned responses are blocked by the presence of a novel stimulus evoking an orienting reflex which inhibits all behaviour other than exploratory responses.

The changes in sensory processing during distraction have been examined by the use of electrodes chronically implanted in the brain of non-anæsthetized and unrestrained animals. Recording from the cochlear nucleus of the cat before habituation, both Galambos (1958) and Hernandez-Peon (1956) examined the effects of visual and olfactory distracting stimuli on auditory evoked potentials. When the cat is presented with a mouse in a glass jar or with fish odours blown into the cage, the high amplitude auditory responses are immediately reduced in amplitude when the cat orients towards the source of distraction. The effect is as if the animal had suddenly shifted from a naïve to a habituated state with regard to the auditory evoked responses. On removal of the distracting stimulus and after the cat ceases orienting, the evoked responses return to their initial high amplitude (see Fig. 3). The duration of interruption of auditory sensory input almost coincides with the period during which the cats are orienting to the distracting stimulus.

It seems from these observations that this focusing of attention on the

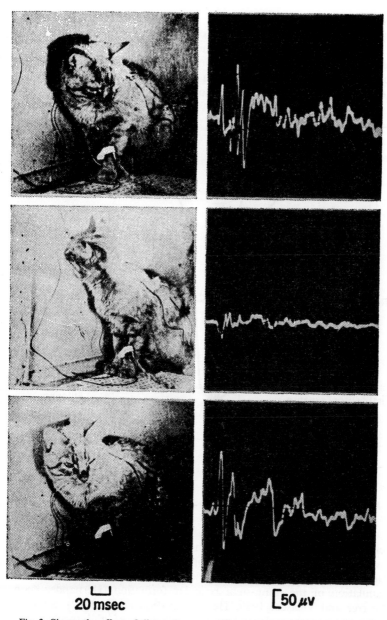

20 msec   50 μv

Fig. 3. Shows the effect of distraction on tactile evoked potentials recorded from the lateral column of the spinal cord during attention elicited by an olfactory stimulus. The records were taken (a) when the cat was relaxed; (b) when the cat was attentively sniffing fish odour delivered through a tube in the cage; (c) when the cat was relaxed again after the odour was removed. From Hernandez-Peon (1961).

distracting stimulus depends upon the active exclusion of irrelevant information. Its transmission in the central nervous system is attenuated at the level of the first synapse in the afferent pathway. The fact that a clear reduction of auditory evoked potentials recorded from the cochlear nucleus is obtained from stimulation of the reticular formation indicates the likelihood of a reticular formation involvement in attentional shifts or sensory attenuation at the level of the first synapse (Hernandez-Peon,

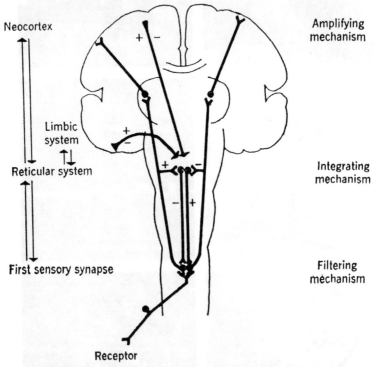

Fig. 4. Schematic representation of some of the main neuronal circuits involved in the transmission and integration of sensory impulses. From Hernandez-Peon (1961).

Scherrer and Jouvet, 1956; Killam and Killam, 1958, 1959; Brust-Carmona *et al.*, 1960). This hypothesis is supported by reports of attenuation of visual evoked responses in the lateral geniculate body by stimulation of the brain-stem reticular formation (Hernandez-Peon, Scherrer and Velasco, 1956; Hernandez-Peon *et al.*, 1957). Similarly Arden and Söderberg (1959) have found evidence of inhibitory afferents to the lateral geniculate body which probably have a reticular origin (Arden and Söderberg, 1961). Hernandez-Peon has concluded from this evidence that "the reticular mechanisms of sensory filtering are formed by a feedback loop, with an ascending segment from second-order sensory neurons to the reticular formation and a descending limb in the opposite direction (Fig. 4). Such an arrangement would prevent over-activation to sensory neurons and, therefore, an excessive bombardment of the brain by afferent impulses. . . . The exclusion of afferent impulses from sensory receptors takes place just as they enter the central nervous system. Therefore the first sensory synapse functions as a valve where sensory filtering occurs."

A great deal of criticism has been engendered by this notion of sensory filtering at the level of the first sensory synapse. As a result of much critical work it would appear that in general the model of sensory filtering proposed by Hernandez-Peon is far too simple. The model takes no account of the fact that there is additional feedback control of afferent input at the receptor itself. Control of retinal discharge by modification of the pupillary diameter due to stimulation of the reticular formation has been demonstrated by Naquet *et al.* (1960) and also by Fernandez-Guardiola *et al.* (1961). If the eye is atropinized, evoked responses in the optic tract and the lateral geniculate body remain constant although cortical responses are in fact attenuated by stimulation of the reticular formation. It is concluded that reticular inhibitory attenuation therefore probably does not take place at the first sensory synapse alone as stated by Hernandez-Peon. Similarly Hugelin, Dumon and Paillas (1960) have shown that reticular control of the cochlear nucleus is due to changing the tension of the middle ear muscles, rather than a direct effect on the cochlear nucleus. Moushegian *et al.* (1961), however, have demonstrated habituation and attenuation of evoked responses at the auditory cortex in cats deprived of middle ear muscles (Fig. 5). Further, Gershuni *et al.* (1960) have confirmed the reports of attenuation of cochlear responses during distraction. Simultaneous records of the cochlear microphonic potential gave no indication of any change suggesting alterations in the tension of the tympanic muscles.

Criticism of an entirely different sort has been advanced against the notion that attention shifts involve exclusion of sensory information. Horn (1960) has pointed out that the possibility of "within modality occlusion" has not been considered. Thus attenuation of evoked responses to clicks in Hernandez-Peon's experiment could be due to the fact that the cat was listening to sounds from the mouse as well as looking at it. He found a reduction in flash-evoked responses of the cat's visual cortex, when a mouse was revealed against a flicker background. This attenuation occurred only if the presentation was made within "attention" periods and was absent if the cat ignored the mouse. Thus reduction in amplitude of evoked responses was taken by Horn as an indication of attention rather than as being caused by exclusion of sensory evoked responses.

This finding, though intriguing, is not without its difficulties of evaluation. It would appear to be at variance with the typical characteristics of attention as reported in the literature. Galambos (1958) and Hearst *et al.* (1960) have found that when a habituated and presumably insignificant stimulus is paired with cutaneous shock, there is a marked increase in the amplitude of the evoked potentials. In other words, the evoked responses produced by a stimulus seem to be increased during orienting and not attenuated, unless by habituation or by shifts of attention.

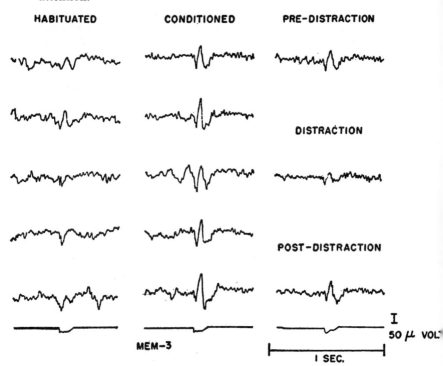

HABITUATED   **CONDITIONED**   **PRE-DISTRACTION**

DISTRACTION

POST-DISTRACTION

MEM-3

I
50 μ VOL.
I SEC.

Fig. 5. Evoked responses to click stimulation at auditory cortex during habituation, conditioning and distraction in cats with middle ear muscles removed. From Moushegian *et al.* (1961).

Mechanisms involved in redundancy learning The storage of information involved in habituation may last for days or even years (Griffith, 1924). Attention shifts, on the other hand, appear to be of a transitory nature restricted to immediate features of the stimulus situation.

The mechanism of the two processes seems clearly to involve inhibitory influences, possibly of reticular origin. Observations on the action of barbiturate anæsthesia indicate that there is a release from inhibitory influences which act tonically during wakefulness upon subcortical levels of the specific afferent pathways (Hagbarth and Kerr, 1954;

Hernandez-Peon, Scherrer and Velasco, 1956; Hagbarth and Höjeberg, 1957). It was shown by Hernandez-Peon and Brust-Carmona (1961) that barbiturate anæsthesia prevented the development of habituation. But, when the animal had been habituated before the administration of pentobarbitone, there was a dramatic loss of habituation and recovery of the original responses. Most interesting of all was the fact that upon recovery from anæsthesia the responses again became attenuated as they had been beforehand. This effect of barbiturates in producing a state of dehabituation, suggests that the origin of the inhibition involved is likely to be reticular. Hernandez-Peon and Brust-Carmona (1961) found that decortication had no effect on the acquisition of habituation of post-rotatory nystagmus. In fact, decorticated cats required fewer trials than normal cats for complete inhibition of ocular movements. Similar results were obtained in animals in which the brain-stem had been transected at the mid-collicular level, indicating that habituation did not involve the thalamic station of the vestibular pathway. Further extensive lesions in the mesencephalic tegmentum did not prevent habituation. Lesions at a pontine level, however, did prevent inhibition of post-rotatory nystagmus. Habituation could not then be obtained. A similar picture was found for tactile habituation of sensory responses within the lateral columns of the spinal cord in the mid-collicular preparation. With severance of the spinal cord at C2, there was a loss of habituation indicating an absence of descending inhibition from the lower brain-stem reticular formation. It is clear from these experiments that the mechanism of habituation is reticular. Further experiments are needed to clarify whether both the encoding and storage of information that is involved in habituation is performed by reticular mechanisms. Certainly there does not seem to be any cortical participation in this type of learning such as that suggested by Sokolov.

III. Associative Learning

Associative learning involves the acquisition by one stimulus of some of the behavioural or functional characteristics evoked by another stimulus. The significance or meaning of a stimulus is altered by virtue of its consistent association with a second stimulus. Data processing of this kind is diametrically opposed to redundancy learning, in that it results in an accentuation of a stimulus by adding to its information value. Such learning enables the animal to attach significance to stimuli. This is most clearly seen in Pavlov's (1928) studies of salivary conditioning. Here the paired presentation of a neutral stimulus (CS) with a food stimulus (US) results in the CS acquiring some of the stimulus properties of the food. This is indicated by the fact that, after several pairings of the CS and US, the CS alone will lead to salivation. Whenever two sets of stimuli occur at the same time, they can then be associated. Pavlov was able to demonstrate a considerable temporal range under which conditioning could occur. He reported that in delayed conditioning procedures, the CS could precede the US by as much as 30 minutes. Such delayed conditioning is, however, only possible with elaborate and special training, and in no way represents the normal operating conditions under which associative bonds are formed between stimuli. In fact, the normal optimal conditions for such data processing are remarkably restricted.

Nature of conditioning   At one time it was believed that conditioning involved the establishment of associative connexions between the CS and the response utilized in the experiment. The conditioned response (CR) was assumed to be simply the same as the response produced by the US. This appears not to be the case. The CR is never a duplicate of the unconditioned response (UR), and only seems to be because of imprecise measurement or incomplete recording of the details of the reaction. Pavlov seldom reported the temporal course of the pattern of salivation. Konorski (1948) has shown that with detailed recording, differences between the CR and the UR become manifest. These clear differences in response sharpen the issue as to what changes occur during conditioning. With regard to learning, the CR has been considered either as a fractional component of the UR that has been conditioned to the CS, or as a preparatory response conditioned to the arrival of the US.

Considering the CR as a fractional component response goes part of the way towards explaining why the CR often seems to be weaker, or to reflect only certain aspects of the UR. For example, where the UR to food consists of salivation, chewing, swallowing, and tail-wagging, the CR may consist of only one or two of these response components. Similarly in fear conditioning, the CR may consist of an autonomic discharge only, without the vocalization, violent skeletal muscle reaction, defæcation, etc., that comprised the UR to shock.

An alternate view of the CR is to regard it as a preparatory response conditioned to the occurrence of the US. The reports where the CR in no way resembles the UR provide evidence in support of this view. The preparatory nature of the CR in salivary conditioning has been described in detail by Zener (1937) from film records taken during conditioning. The CR is seen to involve movements best categorized as food orienting responses to the CS. With the exception of salivation, the CR could in no way be considered a fractional component of the UR. In fact, it included restless movements that were unrelated to the UR. The same sort of thing is true for passive avoidance conditioning where the CR is totally different from the UR to shock.

It is clear from this consideration of the nature of the CR that the response change is of necessity somewhat arbitrary. The main reason for this would seem to be in the nature of the learning which is of the form of an association between stimuli. Where an indifferent stimulus (CS) correlates highly with an effective stimulus (US), it acquires some of the properties of the stimulus with which it is associated. This change in the functional significance of the CS is measured indirectly by the resultant change in response (CR).

Although conditioning involves the formation of associations

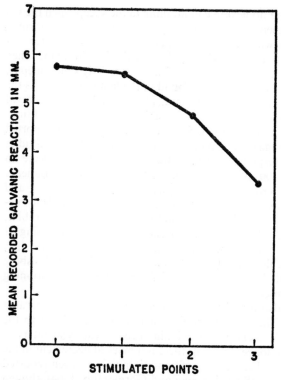

Fig. 6. Stimulus-generalization gradient which shows the amount of spread of GSR conditioned to tactile stimulation of the shoulder (point 0) to the back (point 1), the thigh (point 2) and the calf (point 3). (Bass and Hull, 1934.)

between stimuli, it does not result in a specific stimulus association. This is contrary to habituatory learning where the stimulus redundancy is highly specific. Training to a specific CS results in the conditioning generalizing widely to other similar stimuli. This generalization is only loosely related to the degree of similarity between the CS and test stimuli, as can be seen in Fig. 6. Similar broad generalization gradients have been found by Anrep (1923) for salivary conditioning in the dog. This generalized nature of the association probably enables the learning to be applied over a variety of differing situations.

Time factors governing encoding   Pavlov (1928) regarded the "simultaneous" presentation of the CS and the US as the optimal condition for the acquisition of conditioning. By "simultaneous", Pavlov referred to a time interval of 0–5 sec. between the CS and the US. Subsequent research, using a wide variety of different species and response measures, also points to a remarkably restricted interval as optimal.

Cohen (1950) found no flexion conditioning in the sheep when the CS and the US were presented simultaneously. This finding was confirmed and extended by Fitzwater and Riesman (1952), and by Fitzwater and Thrush (1956) using finger withdrawal conditioning in man. They also pointed out that when the CS–US pairing was strictly simultaneous, transitory signs of conditioning were found in the first few trials. As the training continued, this effect disappeared. The optimal CS–US interval was found to be 400 msec.; it was not possible to obtain any conditioning if the CS occurred after the US. Similar findings have been reported by Spooner and Kellogg (1947), Wolfle (1930) and Wolfle (1932). Studies using the eye blink response as a measure of conditioning indicate an optimal interval of 400 msec. $\pm$ 150 msec. (Bernstein, 1934; Boneau, 1958; Hansche and Grant, 1960; Kimble, 1947; Kimble, Mann and Dufort, 1955; McAllister, 1953a, b). Recently Schneiderman and Gormezano (1964) have shown, using the nictitating membrane in the rabbit, that the optimal interval is 250 msec. Reports on the conditioning of the galvanic skin response indicate an optimum of 450 msec. (Moeller, 1954; White and Schlosberg, 1952). Finally, Kappauf and Schlosberg (1937) reported that the optimal interval for respiratory conditioning in the rat was 600 msec.

Conditioning is also found when the CS and the US are separated by longer periods. The rate of acquisition is inversely related to the length of the CS–US interval. Conditioning occurs readily at intervals up to 1 sec., but with longer intervals there is a marked decrement in the acquisition rate. Nonetheless, signs of conditioning have been reported at intervals up to 4 sec. (Schneiderman and Gormezano, 1964), though at a minimal level. The observations on the optimal CS–US interval show a remarkable degree of uniformity, and further support the notion that conditioning depends on stimulus associations.

Limiting conditions affecting associative learning   The mechanisms concerned in associative learning entail more than mere temporal factors. The sequential order of the stimuli is also important. If the US precedes the CS even fractionally, then no conditioning is found (Cason, 1935; Porter, 1938; Spooner and Kellogg, 1947; Fitzwater and Riesman, 1952). Some evidence has been found for slight and transitory associative bonds being formed (Dostalek and Figar, 1956; Astratyan, 1961). It is most likely, however, that the learning that takes place is "pseudoconditioning" rather than the development of a true conditioned association between the CS and US.

Sokolov (1960) has indicated that there is a complex interaction between the orienting response and the specific response produced by the CS and the US respectively. Habituation of orienting responses to the CS can affect the development of conditioning. A series of experiments by Egger and Miller (1962) have underscored the informative role that is necessary for a stimulus to serve as an effective CS. If in a conditioning procedure CS-1 and CS-2 are successively presented with the US, CS-2 will be redundant in this sequence. Only CS-1 conveys any information, and it is the only stimulus that is conditioned. However, if CS-1 is presented occasionally without CS-2 and the US, then CS-2 becomes a more reliable indicator of the US and is no longer redundant. In these circumstances, it is CS-2 that is conditioned. Hence conditioning occurs only to a CS that is informative; where a stimulus is redundant, it does not become an effective CS and presumably becomes disregarded.

The interaction between orienting and conditioning is further illustrated by the influence of motivation on encoding of information. This has for long been an issue of great controversy in behaviour theory. It is accepted that the performance of a learned task is affected by the motivational level, but what has not been clear is whether the learning *per se* is influenced by motivation. Tolman (1932) claimed that learning in non-motivated animals is not overtly manifested in terms of performance because of a lack of incentive. He argued that learning as distinct from performance was independent of motivational factors. Evidence in support of this was found in experiments where animals exposed to a learning situation in the absence of any motivational factors manifested no signs of conditioning. With the introduction of motivational incentives, however, dramatic evidence of prior *latent learning* was found (Blodgett, 1929; Tolman and Honzik, 1930; Lashley, 1918; Meehl and MacCorquodale, 1948; Muenzinger and Conrad, 1953). One of the main difficulties in resolving this issue has been that in the complete absence of any motivating factors, it is difficult to obtain any active behaviour from an animal, and therefore virtually impossible to expose him to a learning situation. In consequence it has been suggested that the conditions in the latent learning experiments did not fully exclude motivational influences (Miller, 1961). Debold, Jenson and Miller (1965) examined the effect of manipulating the motivational state on the encoding of information during conditioning. Animals were conditioned to lick to a flickering light. Both the recording and the reinforcement of the response were achieved by a small cannula implanted in the roof of the mouth. Their results indicate that learning occurs only in motivated animals. Furthermore, the importance of motivational factors for retrieval of learning was demonstrated. Animals that had been conditioned, failed to show any retention of learning when not motivated. Their results convincingly reveal that both learning and performance are dependent on the presence of motivational factors.

Stability of associative conditioning   Once established, the effects of conditioning appear to be permanent. Numerous studies have demonstrated the great stability of conditioning. There is an almost complete lack of forgetting over a period of time amounting to several years (Liddell *et al.*, 1934; Marquis and Hilgard, 1936; Hilgard and Humphreys, 1938; Wendt, 1936; Kellogg and Wolf, 1939). From this evidence it is quite clear that there is no loss of conditioning due to mere passage of time. If the CS is repeatedly presented without the reinforcing presence of the US, there is a progressive loss of the effects of conditioning, termed extinction, until eventually the CR disappears. Extinction does not represent a loss of information, but seems to resemble to some extent an inhibitory state (Hull, 1943). This is because an extinguished response, without any subsequent retraining, will recover spontaneously with just rest alone (Pavlov, 1928). In addition, conditions which increase inhibition will also accelerate the process of extinction. Massed extinction trials lead to faster extinction than do distributed trials (Hilgard and Marquis, 1935). In contrast, massed training trials lead to slower acquisition of learning compared with distributed practice (Calvin, 1939; Reynolds, 1945; Vandermeer and Amsel, 1952; Spence and Norris, 1950). This effect has been attributed to a build-up of inhibition (Hovland, 1936). The inhibitory nature of extinction is shown by the fact that the extinction process is accelerated when the effort requirements of the CR are increased (Mowrer and Jones, 1943; Solomon, 1948). Finally, if the process of extinction is continued after the CR has ceased to occur, the amount of spontaneous recovery is proportionately reduced (Pavlov, 1928). The inhibitory state that is established during extinction can be *disinhibited* by the presentation of a novel stimulus. This recovery from extinction is transitory. A single reinforcement of the CS by the US can restore the conditioning completely (Soloveychik, 1940). Thus in many respects the processes of extinction and habituation have similar properties. Certainly it seems that once a stimulus is conditioned, extinction does not impair storage of the information but alters its availability.

Neural mechanisms   According to the traditional Pavlovian viewpoint the process of associating stimuli occurs at the level of the cerebral cortex. Pavlov's judgment, that conditioning is impossible in the absence of the cortex, was based on the failure of Zeliony in 1912 to establish conditioning in dogs after complete removal of the cerebral cortex (Zeliony, 1929).

Subsequent experimentation has indicated that both the encoding and storage of associative learning is independent of the cortex. Complete bilateral ablation of the cortical projection areas of either the CS or the US, or removal of the cortex between them, has no effect on the acquisition or retention of conditioning. The sole effect of this type of lesion is to produce impairment of complex and delicate discriminating powers. For example, complete bilateral ablation of the auditory cortex caused amnesia for a simple pitch discrimination post-operatively, which was recovered with retraining. Clear deficits were found for both retention and relearning for tonal pattern discriminations (Butler, Diamond and Neff, 1957). It would appear therefore that the CS and the US cortical projection areas are not necessary for conditioning but are required for delicate differentiation of stimuli.

Another approach to the anatomy of associative learning is that of Doty (1958), and Doty and Giurgea (1961), following the earlier approach of Loucks (1933), and Light and Gantt (1936). These workers used direct stimulation of areas of sensory cortex as a CS and also stimulation of motor cortex as US in an attempt to isolate pathways involved in conditioning. Doty, Rutledge and Larsen (1956) conditioned leg flexion to the stimulation of various cortical areas as CS. Good evidence of transfer was obtained when animals, previously conditioned to stimulation of a specific cortical sensory area, were tested with a peripheral CS of the same sensory modality, suggesting that the mechanisms involved in learning by cortical stimulation were comparable to those of the usual peripheral procedure. Ablation of the cortical region to which the CS had been applied did not disturb transfer of the response to stimulation of corresponding contralateral cortical zones, indicating that the CS region itself was not essential for conditioned performance. Transcortical pathways were not essential, since circumsection of the area did not abolish the response, nor were callosal fibres necessary, because transfer occurred readily between corresponding cortical points even when callosal section was performed before testing. Finally Doty and Giurgea (1961) found that after complete section of the corpus callosum a CR could be established with the CS delivered to one hemisphere and the US to the other. Clearly a subcortical mechanism is involved.

The lack of relevance of cortical function for the formation of stimulus associations is seen most clearly in experiments concerned with conditioning in completely decorticate animals. Poltyrev and Zeliony (1930) repeated their early experiments finding that decortication did not prevent the formation of conditioning of auditory and visual CS to a US of electric shock. In two animals, in fact, pitch discrimination was obtained between a whistle and a knock on wood. Similar results by Lebedinskaia and Rosenthal (1935) were obtained for salivary conditioning to an auditory CS (metronome). In these animals the decortication was subtotal with some sparing of cortex. The numerous studies of conditioning in decorticate animals since that time leave no doubt that such learning is possible in the complete absence of the cortex (Culler and Mettler, 1934; Ten Cate, 1934; Poltyrev, 1936; Zeliony and Kadykov, 1938; Girden, Mettler, Finch and Culler, 1936; Wing and Smith, 1942; Wing, 1946, 1947; Bromiley, 1948). These reports, covering both positive and negative reinforcement conditions, show subcortical learning mechanisms for the conditioning of visual, auditory, thermal, and tactile stimuli.

Girden *et al.* (1936) drew attention at an early stage to the fact that there are certain differences between learning in normal and in decorticate animals. The responses conditioned to the CS in the decorticate animal are diffuse and less specific than are those in the normal animal. Bromiley (1948) has indicated that the diffuse nature of the CR in the decorticate animal is due to the high emotional reactivity of animals so treated. If care is taken to present the training trials only whilst the animal is not aroused, then not only can discrete CRs be established, but also simple powers of discrimination can readily be established.

Very few reports are available concerning the effects of decortication on the retention of previously established associations. Sager, Wendt, Moisanu and Cirnu (1956) have reported that there is no loss of conditioning, although there is a profound change in the CR. When decorticate dogs were presented with an auditory CS paired with shock, they no longer demonstrated a coordinated leg withdrawal; this indicates a loss of the CR. There was no loss of the conditioned significance of the CS. This is indicated by the fact that presentation of the (CS) tone produced a strong affective reaction, which was shown by bristling of the hair (piloerection), dilatation of pupils, rapid breathing (tachypnœa), growling and barking. This agitated reaction shows again the importance of considering associative learning in terms of a change in stimulus significance. The loss of the flexion response not only does not indicate memory loss, but suggests rather a motor deficit due to loss of cortex. The exaggerated nature of the emotional response would reflect the hyperreactive nature of decorticate animals due to the absence of cortical inhibitory control over affective responses. The survival of conditioning following decortication has been shown also by Russell, Kleinman and Plotkin (1965) who found that functional decortication by means of spreading depression did not produce a loss of previously established avoidance conditioning. In a recent study, Hernandez-Peon and Brust-Carmona (1961) compared the relative ease of conditioning under both positive and negative reinforcement conditions in normal and decorticate cats. Conditioning was found to be just as easy to establish as in normal animals. Small lesions in the posterior part of the mesencephalic reticular formation were found to abolish conditioning and to prevent the formation of any stimulus associations.

Doty, Beck and Kooi (1959) found that lesions in the centromedian nucleus of the thalamus, the posterior hypothalamus and mamillary bodies, completely abolished conditioning; whereas large lesions in the medial mesencephalic or antero-medial thalamic and antero-medial hypothalamic areas produced transitory deficits of conditioning which recovered with retraining. Yoshii and Hockaday (1958), Segundo, Roig and Sommer-Smith (1959) and Beck, Doty and Kooi (1958) have also noted interference in conditioning of evoked potentials from lesions in the region of the centromedian nucleus of the thalamus. It may be relevant that Nauta and Kuypers (1958) have indicated that the reticular formation branches into three in this area, giving pathways to the hypothalamus, the limbic system and the thalamic reticular nuclei, each of which has separate relays to the cortex.

The evidence obtained from changes in evoked responses recorded during conditioning is in agreement with the view that associative learning is both encoded and stored at a subcortical level. Once conditioning has been established, the CS is found to produce potential changes in the cortical projection areas of both the CS and the US. Before conditioning, evoked potentials are obtained to the CS solely in the appropriate specific cortical area (Yoshii, 1957; Jouvet and Hernandez-Peon, 1957; Buser and Rougeul, 1956). These findings suggest a subcortical routing of sensory signals such that the CS can acquire functional influence over the cortical projection area of the US. The simultaneous appearance of evoked responses throughout the diencephalon (Yoshii, 1957) suggests it is at this level that the conditioned information is divided, reaching both CS and US projection areas. Thus both specific and non-specific pathways are involved. Moreover Yoshii, Pruvot and Gastaut (1957) have shown that conditioned electrical potentials in the brain are earlier in onset, larger in amplitude and more constant in the mesencephalic reticular formation.

The importance of subcortical mechanisms is shown by the disruptive effects of stimulation of the majority of specific and non-specific structures, such as the thalamus, hypothalamus, hippocampus and the reticular formation (Bloch and Hebb, 1956; MacLean *et al.*, 1955). Glickman (1958) has also reported that rats stimulated in the mid-brain reticular formation immediately after receiving a painful shock at the food tray, completely forgot the preceding experience and promptly returned to the source of the food. Even more interesting is the fact that stimulation of the hypothalamus or the reticular formation of the mid-brain may facilitate as well as inhibit conditioning. Grastyan, Lissak and Kekesi (1956) have demonstrated that stimulation of certain parts of the brain-stem facilitates conditioning, whilst simultaneously inhibiting an antagonistic reflex. For example, they reported facilitation of positively reinforced conditioning and simultaneous inhibition of negatively reinforced conditioning. In many ways the most plausible attempt at synthesizing the current status of experimentation concerning the mechanisms of associative learning, is that proposed by Gastaut (1958). He proposes a model which emphasizes the role of the diencephalic and mesencephalic reticular formation in conditioning, as can be seen in Fig. 7, which shows the mechanisms of stimulus association (closure)

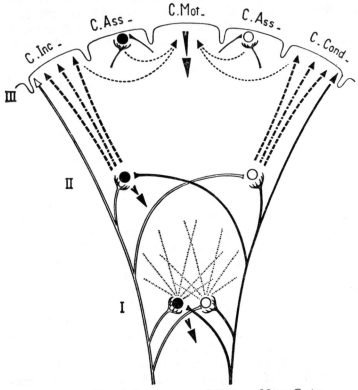

C.Inc. = Unconditioned Cortex   C.Mot. = Motor Cortex
C.Ass. = Association Cortex   C.Cond. = Conditioned Cortex

Fig. 7. Schematic diagram of the differing levels of neural function involved in the formation of stimulus associations in classical conditioning. I Reticular formation of the lower brain-stem. II Thalamic reticular formation. III Cerebral cortex. From Gastaut (1958).

and hierarchical involvement (projection). As can be seen, he conceives of the establishment of a reticular focus of excitation by way of collaterals from the afferent paths for both CS and US. It is suggested that the mechanism of stimulus association involves synaptic convergence of successive stimuli on neurons of the brain-stem reticular formation. This conclusion is supported by numerous macro- and microelectrode studies of responses within the reticular formation to different collateral inputs. Evoked responses within the reticular formation, following brief auditory, visual, tactile or pain inputs, have the same form, regardless of which of these different sensory modalities has been activated. Microelectrode recordings of units within the reticular formation show that such diverse sensory inputs can excite discharges in the same groups of cells (Palestini, Rossi and Zanchetti, 1957; Bradley and Mollica, 1958). Further, French, von Amerongen and Magoun (1952) have shown that if responses to different sensory modalities are presented close together in time, an occlusive interaction of the reticular response occurs. This occlusion indicates that the collaterals feed into a common cell population, as Gastaut indicates in his model. In fact, it would seem as though the time interval for occlusive interaction and the optimal CS–US interval are similar. Thus spatio-temporal convergence may well determine the optimal CS–US interval for the encoding of associative conditioning. This functional "connexion" enables the establishment of what Gastaut calls "plastic traces" in the thalamic reticular formation, which appears to be the probable site of storage.

Both rostral and caudal projections are also involved in this mechanism of closure. The role of the cortex, which depends on thalamo-cortical projections, is to modulate the response manifestations of conditioning. This is achieved by inhibitory control over affective systems in the normal animal, and also by allowing greater selectivity of response to the CS.

IV. Contingency Learning

Information processing, such as is involved in contingency learning provides the basis for the greater part of behaviour in the learning of what to do in a given situation, that is, in learning what responses are instrumental in obtaining rewards and in avoiding punishment. Such learning involves a contingency analysis by the brain of the consequences of behaviour. Such consequences or *reinforcement contingencies*, can be thought of as a strengthening of stimulus–response relationships by increasing the probability of recurrence of the appropriate response when an animal is faced with the same situation again: since in such learning the response that is to be learned must occur before it can be reinforced, then it follows that this response must be within the existing range of responses in the animal's behavioural repertoire. The learning involves a strengthening of the appropriate response so that it occurs promptly and reliably in the situation.

An obvious question concerns the origin of the responses in such learning, since they seem to be released by the animal independently of any identifiable external stimulus. For this reason Skinner (1938) has classed such behaviour as emitted acts or *operants*, to distinguish them from reactions evoked by distinctive stimuli. Such responses are not always entirely random, such as would be involved in a trial-and-error process. Cats in a puzzle-box on the first trial or so generally spend a great deal of time clawing through the bars towards the food. Similarly rats in a Skinner box commonly explore all corners and projecting aspects of the box. In many cases these are orienting responses to environmental stimuli. In others they are clearly outcomes of previous experience or reactions to specific motivational factors. A typical result of a drive state such as hunger or thirst is an increase in the animal's restless behaviour. Such an animal is not only more active, but also more variable in its initial response interactions with the environment. Hence the likelihood of the correct response occurring is increased.

Nature of response   In viewing contingency learning in terms of the formation of stimulus–response dependencies, one does not mean the formation of specific response connexions. An animal performing a learned task very rarely manifests a fixed and stereotyped response pattern, since what is learned does not involve any specific motor outflow. Behavioural evidence for this is seen in experiments where the animals are tested for retention of learning under conditions that require a pattern of responding entirely different from that in the test situation. Macfarlane (1930) trained animals to run through a complex maze correctly, and then required them to swim through the same maze when flooded with water. No increase in errors was found. Similarly Evans (1936) found that rats that had been trained to swim through a maze showed perfect retention when required to run through the same maze. Lashley and McCarthy (1926) found no evidence of impairment in retention of maze learning in rats with cerebellar damage that produced tremor and spasticity. Further, Dorcus and Gray (1932) interfered with the response pattern by removing some of the muscles and limbs of animals after learning. This had no apparent effect on retention.

Perhaps the most searching demonstration of the independence of contingency learning from any specific motor outflow is seen in the experiments involving lesions in the motor cortex. For example, monkeys were trained on a variety of latch-box problems and then various types of lesions were made in motor and pre-motor cortex. After recovery the animals were found to have perfect retention of the learning (Lashley, 1924; Jacobsen, 1932; Glees and Cole, 1950). The lesions in no way affected the recognition of the problem, in that there was no loss of the knowledge of the mechanical operations required. The animals simply utilized new muscle systems to solve the problems.

From these experiments it is clear that contingency learning cannot be analysed in terms of discrete stimulus–response connexions. Rather than attempting to analyse a conditioned response into motor components, we should recognize that in the majority of contingency learning situations the response is defined only in operational terms. What is a correct response in a Lashley jumping stand is totally different from a correct choice in a maze or Skinner box. It is pointless to attempt an analysis in terms of muscle groups involved when by definition the nature of response is characterized by the animal's attainment or non-attainment of an objective. Where this is the case, as it is for this type of learning, then the sensory processing of information must be concerned with the outcome of response sequences or actions.

Reinforcement and encoding   A most important limiting factor for the encoding of contingency learning is the range of conditions under which reinforcement of behaviour is effective. Only responses immediately preceding the attainment of a reward are reinforced. If the reward precedes the response even by no more than a second it is ineffective (Nagaty, 1951b). In the case of negative reinforcement situations, such as learning to escape from an electric shock, the response must precede the reinforcement contingency of shock termination. Information on the precise nature of the optimal interval of time between responses and subsequent reinforcement suggests at first that this is a non-critical factor. Intervals of 30 sec. (Watson, 1917; Perin, 1943), 120 sec. (Perkins, 1947) and even as long as 15 min. (Wolfe, 1934) have been reported as still permitting conditioning. However, there is reason to doubt the validity of these reports. The general methodology of these studies was to permit a rat to make a contingent response and then to delay the delivery of reinforcement for varying time periods whilst keeping the animal in the goal-box. The major weakness of this type of procedure lies in the fact that the delay chamber can acquire conditioned reinforcing properties by association with the presentation of reward. If this adventitious artefact of delayed reinforcement which is mediated by associative learning is prevented, then it is clear that the response reinforcement interval is quite short. Grice (1948) has shown that with a delay of reinforcement of more than 1 sec. contingency conditioning is severely impaired.

The importance of the relationship between response and reinforcement is seen when this contingency is systematically varied. The contingency between response and reward can be scheduled in a number of ways which produce dramatic and systematic changes in the conditioned response (Ferster and Skinner, 1957). For example, the reinforcement contingency can be scheduled so that a given number of responses are required for each reinforcement. Very large response-reinforcement ratios can be gradually established in this way. What is more dramatic is the effect of this partial reinforcement on the resistance of the conditioning to the effects of extinction.

In associative conditioning, by contrast, partial reinforcement seriously interferes with learning (Razran, 1956). Pavlov (1928) found that pairing the US with the CS less frequently than every second or third trial made conditioning impossible. Similarly in eyelid conditioning, a random 50% reinforcement schedule produced a significant response decrement (Reynolds, 1958; Ross, 1959). Certain reinforcement schedules can be established in contingency learning in such a way that extinction is almost impossible, since the conditioned behaviour assumes a fixated and compulsive quality. The systematic and detailed effect that different reinforcement schedules have been shown to have on responding (Ferster and Skinner, 1957) reveals the essential contingent probability nature of this type of learning. This marked influence of the reinforcement schedule on contingency learning clearly implicates an entirely different type of mechanism for processing data in the brain than that involved in associative conditioning. A simple model along the lines of spatio-temporal convergence of impulses clearly is inadequate as an encoding mechanism. Any encoding mechanism for contingency learning must depend on the behavioural mechanisms involved in contingency reinforcement. Once a response has been established by response–contingent reward and the animal is exposed to partial reinforcement, more than individual response patterns are being strengthened. It could be that what are now being reinforced are the actual response sequences leading to reinforcement (Mowrer and Jones, 1945; Skinner, 1938). Certainly clarification of this issue is one that is crucial for advancing our understanding of the type of data processing involved in contingency learning.

Cortical factors Contingency learning, in contrast to associative learning, appears to be highly dependent on cortical function. Much of Lashley's (1929b) early work on the effect of cortical lesions on the acquisition and retention of conditioning is still relevant. As can be seen in Fig. 8, the effect of cortical lesions on subsequent learning is proportional to the amount of tissue removed and the difficulty of the task. For the simplest maze, only ablation of 50% of the cortex had any measureable effect on learning. For a more complicated maze (maze II) the correlation between the extent of ablation and learning difficulty is clearer, and it is very marked for the most difficult maze. Similarly the ability of rats to learn how to pull a chain to open a door in a latch box, was only disturbed by ablation of more than 50% of the cortex (Lashley, 1917a,b). In all cases the rats' learning ability was not related to any particular area of cerebral cortex.

The same general conclusions were also drawn from the effects of cortical lesions on retention of conditioning. The impairment of retention of previous learning was found to be dependent upon the extent of the cortical loss and independent of its locus. These findings were amply confirmed by Hu (1938) using smaller lesions than Lashley, and by Ericksen (1939a,b), with larger ablations variously distributed in the cortex. Rey (1938, 1939) also showed that small lesions had no

appreciable effect on retention of maze learning, but that lesions of 30%
or successive small lesions amounting to 30% seriously disturbed
retention. From these studies it appears that a lesion of any particular
size leads to greater impairment of retention of conditioning than of
ability to learn a maze. A further consideration is the effect of cortical
lesions on maze-bright and maze-dull rats (Ericksen, 1939a,b). Lesions of

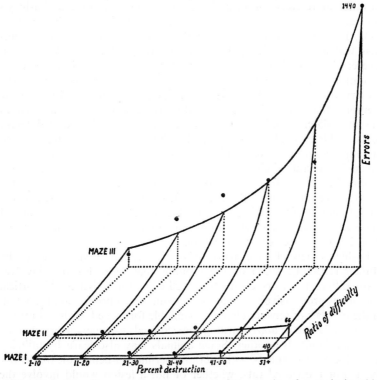

Fig. 8. A three-dimensional representation of the results of a study in which
difficulty of maze was varied, lesions of different sizes were made, and the degree of
retardation (errors) in learning measured. From Lashley (1929b) by permission of the
publishers.

20% had less effect on retention in animals that had learned rapidly
before the operation than on those that had learned slowly. Maze-
bright rats seemed to be able to function better after cortical ablations
than maze-dull animals.

The principal finding of these studies is that the effect of a cortical
lesion on maze learning or retention is proportionate to the mass of
tissue removed. Lashley concluded from this that the cortex is relatively
nonspecific in its role in maze learning. Although admitting the specifi-

city of the primary sensori-motor areas in perceptual and motor skills, respectively, Lashley regarded them as also having, along with other "associative" areas of the cortex, a general function in learning. This general function he termed *mass action*.

At the same time these results also imply that various areas of the cortex are equipotential, or interchangeable in their functional participation in learning. Actually the concept of equipotentiality is applied here to different regions within a given sensory projection area. Lashley's studies of the visual cortex in the rat reveal this most clearly (Lashley, 1935, 1939, 1942). For example, performance in discriminating brightness was affected only by the complete removal of the striate area, whereas lesions of other cortical sectors were ineffective in this type of conditioned discrimination. Further, within the striate cortex, the preservation of a small proportion of tissue prevented total loss of the memory. Since this island of spared cortex could be anywhere within the anterolateral surface of the striate cortex, it is clear that different parts of this cortical sector are equal with regard to their potentiality to maintain conditioned discrimination. Similar experiments involving an isolated remnant of visual cortex for pattern discrimination strikingly confirmed these findings. After conditioning, all of the right visual cortex was removed as well as the entire left, except for a small area of the lateral margin of the striate area. Lashley concluded from the results of these experiments that pattern discrimination is possible with no more than 2% of striate cortex remaining.

Lashley's view of mass action of cortical function was criticized by Hunter (1930a,b; 1931) on the grounds that maze learning involves many different sensory channels as well as motor activities. As cortical ablation is progressively increased, there must be a progressive reduction in the number of sensory channels available for maze learning. Further, it is possible that in maze learning some animals use one sensory channel and other animals another. Some animals may also learn by utilizing several sensory channels, without the experimenter being able to identify them. For individual rats, whether or not a lesion would involve the particular projection area of the sensory channel mediating the learning is purely a matter of chance. The more extensive the lesion, however, the greater the probability of removing tissue involved in learning in the majority of cases. Thus summation of a chance sampling factor could well create the impression that contingency learning and memory depend on the amount of cortex available.

Experimentally it is known that animals vary in the utilization of cues in contingent conditioning such as maze learning (Munn, 1950). Where rats are trained in the light and tested in the dark it has been found that some are considerably impaired and others are not (Dennis, 1929; Finley, 1941). Further, where a maze is used that involves alternative sensory solutions, Kretchevsky (1933) noted that some rats will react consistently to visual cues, others will react to spatial cues and some use both. Progressive sensory channel elimination was found to produce effects on maze learning similar to those of mass action (Honzik, 1936). Loss of the visual channel has little effect on learning, as is shown by blind animals, nor has loss of the olfactory channel much effect in itself. Anosmia and blindness combined, however, results in a marked retardation of learning. The greater the number of sensory channels excluded, the greater the impairment in learning (see Fig. 9).

Tsang (1934, 1936) produced evidence to show that loss of eyesight in a rat resulted in only a slight retardation of maze learning, whereas rats

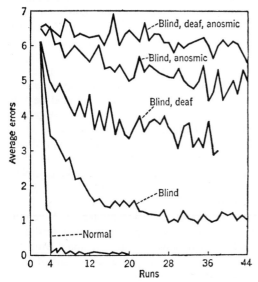

Fig. 9. The effect of exclusion of sensory modalities on the learning of a 14-cul elevated maze (Honzik, 1936).

with the striate cortex removed showed great impairment. This differential effect between peripheral and central blinding was approximately twice as large with an elevated open track maze as with the enclosed alley maze. These results indicated that the striate cortex had, as well as a visual function, a general learning function in accordance with the principle of mass action.

These experiments were criticized by Finley (1941) because the lesions extended beyond purely striate areas and could therefore have involved loss of additional sensory channels in addition to vision. She claimed that the findings of Tsang as well as those of Lashley could just as well support Hunter's sensory channel hypothesis as Lashley's principle of mass action. The experiments were repeated taking care to limit the lesions to the boundaries of the visual cortex. Since demarcation of areas and ablation in a smooth-brained (lissencephalic) animal, such as the rat is never precise, most of Finley's striate removals were inevitably subtotal. Not surprisingly, she found no evidence for mass action. Rats with striate lesions in fact were slightly superior in learning to blinded rats. When animals were tested in the dark where visual cues were irrelevant for learning the maze, rats without striate cortex were just as proficient as normal control animals.

Lashley (1943) believed that Finley's findings were vitiated by a number of factors, the most important of which was that the size of lesion was too small. In his opinion "neither the behavioural nor anatomical data justify the conclusion that there was any significant postoperative interference with vision in the majority of animals." Accordingly Lashley attempted to remove enough of the striate cortex to be sure of producing blindness, without extending beyond the visual area. Rats with striate lesions were found to be more impaired in performance than sightless animals. However, this still does not give decisive evidence of mass action, since once again the lesion extended beyond the visual area. This suggests that the rat brain presents too great a difficulty for precise delimitation of ablations. Using monkeys, where reasonably precise removal of tissue is possible, Orbach (1959) produced the most convincing evidence for mass action. Monkeys were trained on a Lashley type III maze and then made blind. This produced a complete loss of conditioning and retardation of relearning of the maze. The original learning must have involved visual cues exclusively. After relearning the maze, the striate cortex was removed bilaterally. When the animals were subsequently retested a small but significant retardation in relearning the maze was found. It would seem that apart from the visual function of the striate cortex, it also possesses a general non-visual function of the kind regarded as mass action.

Recent developments in neurosurgery and neurophysiology have made it possible to restrict contingency conditioning to one cortical hemisphere (Myers, 1962; Sperry, 1961; Downer, 1962). These experiments have utilized in varying degrees the "split-brain" preparation, where the brain is divided along the mid-line by section of the corpus callosum, the optic chiasma and in some cases the anterior and posterior commissures (see Fig. 10).

The role of the corpus callosum in transferring the effects of conditioning and memory was first indicated by Myers (1955). Chiasma-sectioned cats were trained to discriminate various patterns with one eye covered, thus lateralizing the visual input to one hemisphere. When tested with the opposite eye, which had been covered during conditioning, there was immediate transfer of memory, although the performance was not quite as good as that using the trained side. Later work by Myers (1956) indicated that the degree of this discrepancy depended on the difficulty of the problem. It is clear that the untrained hemisphere could receive visual information of the discrimination at cortical level only via callosal fibres.

Animals, with both chiasmic and callosal fibres sectioned before discrimination training, showed no transfer of conditioning to the

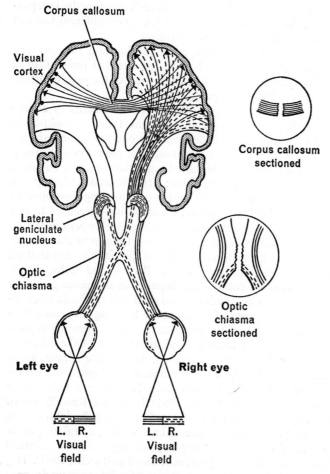

Fig. 10. Diagram of the brain and visual system, showing the points where mid-line sections are made to produce a visually split-brain animal (Downer, 1963).

untrained hemisphere (Myers, 1955; Sperry, Stamm and Miner, 1956; Downer, 1958, 1959). The animals when exposed to the problems with the untrained hemisphere showed no retention of training and there was no saving in the relearning. Similar lateralization to one cortical hemisphere of the effects of a somæsthetic discrimination were found by Stamm and Sperry (1957). If section of the optic chiasma and corpus callosum followed conditioning, no lateralization was found (Downer, 1962). In split-brain animals each cortical hemisphere seems to function as an independent and separate storage system. Trevarthen (1960) has shown that the split-brain monkey is capable of learning simultaneously two different and opposite problems, one in each functionally independent hemisphere. Not only can the animal learn two different tasks at once but it retains each without any confusion.

These demonstrations that contingency learning and memory can proceed independently in each hemisphere indicate that the storage of this type of memory trace must be cortical in view of the purely cortical connexions subserved by the corpus callosum.

Cortical storage of contingency learning is also indicated by experiments using spreading cortical depression to obtain functional split-brain preparations. Cortical function is depressed in one hemisphere during conditioning, and the animals are then tested for retention of learning with the trained hemisphere depressed and the other hemisphere functional (Bureš and Burešová, 1960; Russell and Ochs, 1960). The contingency learning established during conditioning was found to be restricted to the trained hemisphere. Conditioning lateralized to one hemisphere was found to remain restricted unilaterally for periods lasting up to two weeks or more. No evidence of passive transfer of the memory trace to the untrained hemisphere was found, despite the fact that all inter-hemispheric connexions were intact (Russell and Ochs, 1963). In view of the essentially cortical involvement in the propagation of spreading depression (Ochs, 1962) it seems clear that the brain mechanisms involved in the storage of contingency learning are cortical in nature. A dramatic finding of the experiments using spreading depression concerns the nature of inter-hemispheric transfer of the effects of conditioning. A stored memory trace in one hemisphere appears to be inert. Transfer occurred only when the animal performed the conditioned behaviour a few times whilst both hemispheres were active (Bureš and Burešová, 1960; Travis, 1964; Ross and Russell, 1964). Transfer thus required an active process of encoding the information in the untrained hemisphere. If the animal made several responses without any reinforcement contingency during bilateral cortical function, then no transfer was apparent (Russell and Ochs, 1963). This failure to transfer indicates the importance of reinforcement in contingent conditioning.

The nature of the cortical storage of this type of conditioning appears to be diffuse. Myers (1962) found that inter-hemispheric transfer of conditioning in chiasma-sectioned cats did not depend on any specific fibres within the corpus callosum. The effects of sectioning different portions of the callosum revealed that both anterior and posterior bundles within the callosum can be equally effective in the transfer of learning. Further work by Sperry (1956) indicates that cortical localization involved in storage of visual learning is diffuse and not confined to the directly trained receptive area of the cortex.

The fact that transfer of such learning is found in either chiasma-sectioned or callosum-sectioned animals that are trained with one eye covered suggests that the effects of learning are bilaterally represented in both cortical hemispheres. On these grounds Sperry (1964) has suggested that, in fact, the engram is stored bilaterally as a separate and independent memory trace in each cortical hemisphere. Russell, Ross and Strongman (1964) have, however, reported considerable memory loss for visual conditioning from hemidecortication and found no evidence that the loss depended on which hemisphere was removed. This would seem to suggest that storage of contingency conditioning normally involves a single memory trace extending through both hemispheres.

The existence of separate and different storage mechanisms in the brain for associative and contingency learning respectively, may well explain the few reports that have been made of transfer of learning in the split-brain animal (Ross and Russell, 1966). From this point of view it would be expected that associative learning, being stored subcortically, would not be restricted to one hemisphere. In fact, attempts to restrict classical conditioning to one hemisphere have only confirmed this prediction (McCleary, 1960; Meickle, Sechzer and Stellar, 1962; Bureš and Burešovà, 1964; Ross and Russell, 1965). This difference between storage mechanisms has probably not been fully appreciated in the past. In all probability it has been a contributing factor to the difficulties encountered in efforts to elucidate the neural basis of memory.

V. Consolidation of Learning

From the reports of retrograde amnesia in man it seems that a certain period of time is required for memory to be encoded. In retrograde amnesia the loss of memory may obliterate more or less completely the recall of events for a variable period of time preceding the accident or injury. Retrograde amnesia may occur as a result of head injury, electroshock therapy, cerebral anoxia and accidents such as carbon monoxide poisoning. Concussive head blows can often lead to amnesia, where loss of consciousness "is always followed by amnesia for the actual moment of the incident" (Trotter, 1924). In an extensive review of post-traumatic amnesia Russell and Nathan (1946) showed clearly that it was a selective loss of memory for recent events. Even several years of memories can be lost completely, whilst events further back, whether trivial or important are not forgotten and can be recalled without difficulty. Recovery from amnesia occurs not in order of importance but in order of time. The least recent memories recover first. It seems as though the record in the brain at the time of encoding of memory is labile or incomplete in form. Hence these recent memories are more susceptible to impairment by such factors as concussion etc., whereas memories that are fully consolidated in the brain are not susceptible. Unfortunately the interpretation of clinical data concerning retrograde amnesia is made difficult by the lack of knowledge of the changes accompanying concussion. Following concussive accidents the EEG becomes flat, suggesting a reduction in activity of cortical neurons (Larrsen *et al.*, 1954; Meyer and Denny-Brown, 1955) in a way strongly reminiscent of spreading depression (Burns, 1958).

It has been suggested that the neurophysiological processes involved in the formation of stable memory require some time for the neural record to consolidate (Muller and Pilzecker, 1900). Hebb (1949) has suggested that recent memory is based on the reverberation of impulses in neural chains leading to a permanent modification of the excitability of one neuron by another. This reverberatory activity in the brain continues for some time and then gives rise to a permanent growth change. If the initial reverberatory activity were interfered with, or blocked, the permanent change would either not occur or would be incomplete. Hence if this process of consolidation were prevented, permanent learning would not occur. Konorski (1961) has proposed a similar hypothesis in some detail regarding the physiological mechanisms involved. Whether or not reverberatory neuronal activity precedes consolidation of the learning trace is not known. It does, however, seem clear that a certain amount of time is required for consolidation of the effects of learning. If the normal activity of the brain is interfered with, either by electroconvulsive shock (ECS) or anæsthetics, during this consolidation period then there is a memory loss. Duncan (1949) examined the effect of using ECS to block consolidation. Rats were trained once a day to avoidance conditioning in a shuttle box. The animals received ECS at various times following each trial. It was found that the closer the seizure was to the end of each trial the more severe was the memory loss. This general finding has been confirmed and extended to other learning situations by Ransmeier and Gerard (1954), Thompson and Dean (1955), Thompson (1957) and Leukel (1957). All of these findings are compatible with the view that a single ECS can produce memory loss if administered within 15–60 min. after the learning trial. Moreover, when ECS was given immediately after the learning trial, memory of the conditioning was obliterated. Age appears to be a factor in consolidation in that ECS has been found to produce greater loss in young rats than in older ones (Thompson, 1958). An interesting experiment by Thompson *et al.* (1961) demonstrated that a longer consolidation time was required by maze-dull rats than by maze-bright rats. In maze-dull rats ECS was found to produce memory loss over much longer periods after training than was the case for maze-bright rats.

The studies using ECS as a means of interfering with consolidation all involved deficient encoding due to a failure to retain a learned response. Coons and Miller (1960) suggest that this response failure could be due to the possible punishing effects of ECS on the rat. If the shock were felt, then it would produce an avoidance of the response, which would have the appearance of a memory loss.

Madsen and McGaugh (1961), Jarvik (1964) and Heriot and Coleman (1962) found ECS interfered with encoding for avoidance learning. Rats placed on a small elevated platform above ground level received a shock upon jumping off the platform. Retention of this passive avoidance conditioning was shown by the animal staying on the platform after being put back on it. ECS applied after the avoidance conditioning impaired encoding of the effects of shock in that the animals stepped off the platform. If the ECS was delayed, no amnesia was found, since the animals avoided jumping off the platform. This experiment seems to provide decisive refutation of the notion that ECS produces loss of memory because of its punishing properties.

Suggestions have also been made that repeated ECS might cause damaging physiological effects on the brain. Repeated ECS permanently changes task performance (Brady, 1951; Braun, Russell and Patton, 1949a,b), permanently decreases open field activity (Stern, 1956a,b), and alters food motivation (Mirsky and Rosvold, 1953). However, in recent experiments such possible damaging effects due to repeated ECS have been avoided by examining memory loss after a single ECS. Weissman (1963) and Chevalier (1965) found permanent memory losses in the rat following a single ECS given after learning. King (1965) confirmed this and found the effectiveness of the single ECS was maximal just after learning, but progressively declined with increase in time, becoming ineffective when given 60 min. after learning.

Further evidence of the process of consolidation is provided by studies in which anæsthetic drugs were injected at various intervals after each learning trial. Leukel (1957) found impairment in learning when thiopentone was given intraperitoneally 1 min. after each daily trial. If the injection was delayed for 30 min. no such effect was found. In an elegant series of experiments Pearlman, Sharpless and Jarvik (1961) have studied the effect of rapid administration of anæsthetics at various intervals after exposure to a one-trial learning task. Rats were trained to press a bar for water. On reaching a given standard of performance they were punished for responding by receipt of a shock through the bar. Retention of this one-trial avoidance conditioning was shown in control animals the next day by a suppression of the bar-pressing response. Rats that had been anæsthetized by jugular injections of pentobarbitone immediately after conditioning showed almost complete memory loss for the shock the next day. Administration of pentobarbitone after a 20-min. delay caused no memory loss. Similar results have been found using ether administered at various times up to an hour after learning (Abt, Essman and Jarvik, 1961; Essman and Jarvik, 1961). In all cases amnesia or interference with consolidation was exhibited by the animal *failing* to inhibit a conditioned response. If depressant drugs interfere with memory encoding because of their disruptive action on short-term consolidation processes, then any agent that increases the rate of consolidation should improve learning. Lashley (1917b) presented evidence that strychnine would facilitate maze performance in rats, whereas caffeine would impair it. This facilitatory effect of strychnine on maze performance, was confirmed by McGaugh and Petrinovich (1959). It could, however, be due to some transitory facilitatory effect of strychnine on nervous activity during testing. However, McGaugh, Thompson, Westbrook and Hudspeth (1962) and Ross (1964) have found that injections of strychnine given shortly after the learning trials also facilitated learning. Further, the sooner the administration of the drug after the trial, the greater the improvement in performance the following day. It would appear from these results that the continuing (perseverative) processes involved in consolidation had been facilitated or accelerated in some fashion. This conclusion is supported by similar results obtained by post-learning trial injections of either picrotoxin or the stimulant drug 5-7-diphenyl-1-3-diazadamantan-6-ol (1757 I.S.) (Breen and McGaugh, 1961; McGaugh, Westbrook and Thompson, 1962). Further, Pare (1961) found caffeine would facilitate consolidation if administered shortly after learning, but if there was an hour's delay, no facilitatory effect was found. Finally McGaugh, Westbrook and Burt (1961) found that the differential learning rates of maze-bright and maze-dull rats was abolished by administration of 1757 I.S. before learning trials. From these experiments on both the interference and facilitation of consolidation, it is clear that perseverative brain changes are required for the encoding of learning.

The temporal cortex   Memory disturbances related to temporal lobe seizures were noted by Hughlings Jackson (1888). More definitive and recent reports come from neurosurgical ablation of the temporal cortex for the treatment of epilepsy (Milner and Penfield, 1955; Scoville and Milner, 1957). After the operation these epileptic patients had symptoms suggestive of Korsakoff's syndrome (Talland, 1960); they were apparently incapable of processing current experience into memory and had difficulty in recalling events that took place up to 2–3 years before the operation. Earlier memories could still be recalled vividly. This suggests that the temporal lobe must have an important role in the encoding or consolidation of learning rather than in storage.

These clinical observations have been supported to some extent by the studies on experimental temporal lobectomy in animals. Brown and Schäffer, in 1888, reported on the visual memory defects following bilateral temporal cortex ablation in the monkey. In 1938 Klüver and Bucy discovered that temporal lobe ablations produced striking amnesia for visual memories. Monkeys with lesions in the infero-temporal or ventro-temporal neo-cortex seemed unable to recognize familiar objects and were generally deficient in visual tasks. It appears that the "temporal" animal has an amnesia for previously learned visual habits, but can relearn them with retraining (Chow, 1956; Mishkin and Pribram, 1954). Lesions in other cortical regions—preoccipital, frontal, parietal or even the medial surface of the temporal lobe—had no such effects (Mishkin, 1954; Chow, 1952; Wilson, 1957). By the same token it also appears that delayed response and somæsthetic discriminations are unaffected by temporal lesions (Pribram and Barry, 1956; Wilson, 1957). Thus it seems as though the temporal neo-cortex deficits are restricted to visual memories.

This temporal cortex participation in visual discrimination learning raises a host of questions concerning the anatomical basis of this involvement. The work of Chow (1961) suggests that the connexions involved are transcortical rather than thalamocortical. Undercutting the temporal cortex to sever thalamic projections had no effect on retention of visual powers of discrimination, whereas cross-hatching the temporal cortex to cut transcortical connexions did produce visual memory defects of the same degree as ablation of the temporal cortex.

What is harder to understand, however, is the nature of the visual deficit in the "temporal" animal. Whenever a lesion produces a behavioural deficit, there appear to be two possible causes of the deficit (Teuber, 1955). A visual defect could be due to a loss of visual acuity, or to the animal no longer understanding the situation. In the case of the "temporal" animal, the loss of visual memories does not seem to be caused by visual defects. Wilson and Mishkin (1959) found that monkeys with lateral occipital lesions had difficulty in learning string problems and in discrimination of colour patterns, but had no difficulty in form discrimination or with learning-set problems. The behaviour of "temporal" monkeys was exactly the reverse; they had no difficulty with string and pattern tasks, but were retarded in form discrimination and learning-set tasks. It appears that the temporal neo-cortex deficit cannot be attributed to visual defects, particularly as such animals show no sign of having the visual field restricted (scotoma).

Studies to test whether memory loss produced by temporal cortex lesions was due to reduced understanding indicated that this was not the case. Chow (1954) trained monkeys on learning-set problems involving three-dimensional tasks and patterns. After temporal cortex lesions the animals retained the learning-set performance for three-dimensional objects but had a memory deficit for patterns. The retention of the learning-set under some conditions indicates that the animals under-stood what was required in the test situation and were not deficient in the ability to retain the learning-set. The explanation of the loss for the patterns is obscure. Mishkin and Hall (1955) presented evidence that task difficulty in terms of size discrimination is a factor involved in the memory loss of "temporal" animals. Chow and Orbach (1957), how-ever, failed to confirm this when task difficulty was in terms of exposure time of stimuli. The extent of training, however, has been found by Chow and Survis (1958) and Orbach and Fantz (1959) to be a significant factor. Animals were trained on some problems only until they had attained a given standard, but on other problems several hundred over-training trials were given. After temporal cortex removal it was found that the memory loss occurred only in the problems in which the animals had not been over-trained.

The information on the nature of the visual defect following temporal cortex lesions has enabled us to exclude a variety of hypotheses. What actually happens is still very much an open question, but the experiments on temporal cortex removal certainly do not seem to warrant our placing any great confidence in the earlier speculations on its possible role as a site of short-term memory or being involved specifically in consolidation.

Hippocampus More recent experiments, however, indicate that bilateral ablation of the temporal lobes, in particular of the hippocampus, result in memory defects that in general are similar to those described in clinical cases in man. Bilateral hippocampal lesions in the monkey have been shown to impair the acquisition of both visual and auditory discrimination although previously learned tasks are retained (Orbach, Milner and Rasmussen, 1960; Stepien, Cordeau and Rasmussen, 1960). Similar impairment in the learning of delayed responses was found in the cat after bilateral ablation of the hippocampus (Grastyan and Karmos, 1961). Further, Kaada *et al.* (1961) reported retardation in post-operative maze learning in rats with hippocampal lesions. In contrast to these reports Isaacson, Douglas and Moore (1961) found that hippo-campal ablation in rats resulted in an *improvement* in the learning of conditioned avoidance responses. Similarly King (1958) and Tonini (1964) found similar effects from septal lesions. Finally Cordeau and Mahut (1964) showed that amygdalo-hippocampal ablations only impaired visual or auditory learning if the monkeys were tested shortly after the operation: if they were tested two years later no defects were seen. Thus hippocampal damage may only have an initial detrimental effect on learning; with passage of time recovery to pre-operative levels seems possible.

At present it is difficult to account for these apparently conflicting reports concerning the role of the hippocampus in memory consolida-tion. Certainly the facts do not justify the notion that the hippocampus acts as a consolidation mechanism. Green (1964) has suggested that the learning defects that follow hippocampal lesions could be due to a disturbance of attentional mechanisms rather than of encoding mechanisms. Patients, for example, can retain three-digit numbers for several minutes so long as they are not distracted: yet if the investigator leaves the room and returns a short time later, they may fail to remember having seen him. Rather than describe this as a loss of "short-term" memory, Green (1964) suggests that "post distractional amnesia" might be a more accurate term.

Grastyan (1959) has suggested, on the basis of his observations of the effect of stimulation of the hippocampus on conditioning, that the role of the hippocampus may be to prevent distraction. Stimulation of the hippocampal-fornix system would cause an animal to rivet its attention on a stimulus "as if it had been a magnet". In broad agreement with this point of view is the report by Adey *et al.* (1957) that hippocampal stimulation blocks transmission of sensory signals to higher centres. Grastyan and Karmos (1961) have reported increased hippocampal theta activity (4–7 waves per second) during the early stages of learning and a desynchronization of electrical activity in the later phases. Extraneous stimuli causing the animal to make "searching" movements restored theta activity.

Similar observations were made by Adey *et al.* (1960) and Holmes and Adey (1960) during approach conditioning in cats. They studied the phase relationships between theta rhythms in the hippocampus proper and in the adjacent entorhinal cortex. During learning, the appearance of theta waves in the hippocampus preceded their appearance in the temporal cortex, suggesting an information flow from hippocampus to cortex. When the animal is well trained and therefore using recall, the phase relationship is inverted: this suggests a reversed information flow from cortex to hippocampus. Adey and co-workers suggest that these changes in phase relations between cortex and hippocampus may be the basis of a mechanism of recall rather than of consolidation of memory traces.

The prefrontal cortex   The role of the prefrontal areas of the cerebral cortex has been suggested by Jacobsen (1935) to be that of mediating immediate memory. He found, in his now classical experiments, that after removal of the prefrontal areas, monkeys were unable to perform a task involving a delay of several seconds before responding to a stimulus. Typically in these delayed-response problems the animal is given a cue as to the location of a reward (e.g. the placing of a peanut under one of two cups in front of the animal). The animal is restrained for a short time, and then tested to see if it remembers what response to make. Since Jacobsen's discovery, a variety of differing delayed-response tests have been used and invariably it has been found that after ablation of the prefrontal cortex the animal is unable to solve these tasks (Warren and Akert, 1964).

On the basis of the failure of the "prefrontal" animal to solve problems involving a delay, whilst showing normal ability to learn discrimination problems, Jacobsen concluded that these animals had difficulty in remembering information over brief periods of time. This deficit was regarded as a loss of *"immediate memory"*. However, Finan (1939) found that "prefrontal" animals were able to solve a variety of problems involving immediate memory of recent events. It was only in the delayed-response test that the "prefrontal" animals failed. Finan (1942) showed further that if monkeys were given the pre-delay reward from the cup that would normally be correct after the delay, then they could solve the delayed response situation. Using this modified procedure it was possible to induce the "prefrontal" monkey to pay better attention to the stimulus. Hence it appeared that the deficit in the "prefrontal" animal was not one of immediate memory, but rather one of attention. In agreement with this view the "prefrontal" monkey gives the appearance of being easily distracted and inattentive compared with normal animals. It was observed further that "prefrontal" animals under light sedation gave improved delayed-response scores (Wade, 1947; Pribram, 1950 Mishkin, Rosvold and Pribram, 1953). It therefore appeared that distraction, which was reduced by sedation, was responsible for the "prefrontal" animal's failure to solve problems involving delay. A different way of testing this attentional factor was to reduce the factors causing distraction instead of the animal's reactivity. Malmo (1942) found that if "prefrontal" animals were kept in darkness during the delay period, so that all visual distractions were excluded, they could then solve delayed-response problems.

It is not suggested that attentional factors can account entirely for the deficit of the "prefrontal" animal. Many other behavioural characteristics may be affected by this lesion. The point we are concerned with here is that the prefrontal cortex cannot be considered as being directly concerned in the process of memory consolidation. The evidence from temporal and frontal lobe ablations indicates that no area of the cerebral cortex is specifically concerned with consolidation. The highly complex memory functions of these two cortical areas cannot be described simply as short-term memory. In any case this term in some senses seems to have outlived its usefulness.

Comparative aspects   In many areas of physiology, understanding has been broadened by the use of different species to study the development of physiological mechanisms.

From the point of view of comparative anatomy certain definite structural trends can be seen in the evolution of the vertebrate brain. As Fig. 11 illustrates, the size of the brain relative to the spinal cord increases progressively in the vertebrate series from fish to man. At the same time there is a relatively greater increase in the development of the cerebrum and in mammals this trend is further continued by an increase in size of the cerebral cortex in comparison with the rest of the brain. The development of gyri and sulci in the cortex is part of this trend, since the convolutions of the brain permit a greater area of cortical mantle to be contained in a limited space. The calculations of Leboucq (1929) show that in primates the surface area of the convoluted brain is more than twice that of a smooth brain in a skull of the same size.

The increasing importance of the neocortex in the higher vertebrates is indicated by the effects of the removal of the cerebral hemispheres in different species. As the brain develops in size and complexity in the

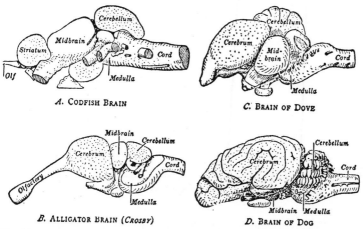

Fig. 11. Successive stages in the evolution of the vertebrate brain (Newman, 1926).

phylogenetic series from fish to man, functions which were originally controlled by lower systems are taken over by the cerebrum. This progressive shift of dominance to the higher centres is called encephalization, which is perhaps the major principle in the evolution of the central nervous system.

Encephalization is apparent in most of the functions of the brain including motor activity, sensory discrimination, and learning. In the absence of the cerebrum, fishes and birds show no obvious signs of motor disturbance, whereas after decortication the rat, the cat, and the dog show increasing signs of motor impairment. The decorticate monkey is the most severely impaired in that it is completely unable to walk. There is a similar trend in the case of vision. Following decerebration there is no apparent impairment of vision in the fish and little change in the bird. The decorticate rat loses pattern vision, but can still distinguish between brightness, position, and distance of objects. The cat, dog, and monkey retain only brightness perception; man becomes completely blind (Marquis, 1935). There seems to be the same trend for the effect of decortication on learning.

Faced with the progressive evolution of the cortex, a major problem for the comparative psychologist has been to evaluate its role in terms of the relative learning capacity or intelligence of the various species. This has not been an easy task. Valid comparisons of learning ability are difficult to make in view of the very great sensori-motor differences that exist between different species. One cannot compare the learning of a rat and a monkey in a task that requires the use of hands. Further-

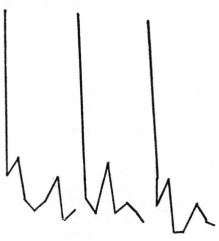

Fig. 12. Relative-error curves for sparrow, rat and monkey (not necessarily in that order) trained in a Hampton Court maze (Bitterman 1960).

more, the problem of motivational variation is considerable: it is hard to obtain conditions giving comparable incentives for widely separated species. The effect of electric shock is quite clear on a mammal but obscure on an animal such as a turtle. From this point of view it is evident that any learning differences found between species might always be accounted for on the basis of motivational differences.

In general, where comparisons of the learning ability of cross-species have been made, the experimental evidence has not in fact indicated any great differences: the learning rates appear to be similar for a wide variety of animals (Razran, 1933). The rate of maze learning is similar for the bird, rat, and monkey (Fig. 12). Indeed Lashley (1929) reports that rats and humans are equally proficient. Even the chimpanzee has not been spared, having been found to be slightly inferior to domestic animals in learning to discriminate visually (Gardner and Nissen, 1948).

These findings seem to support Lashley's (1929) comment: "The comparative study of learning in different animals gives little evidence that evolution has brought any change in the rate of formation of simpler habits. On the other hand, there is a fairly consistent rise in the limits of training and in the formation of complex habits with ascent in the phylogenetic scale."

The work of Boycott and Young (1950) most convincingly supports the fact that simple learning tasks do not reveal differences in the learning rate for the brains of different species. They have shown that the

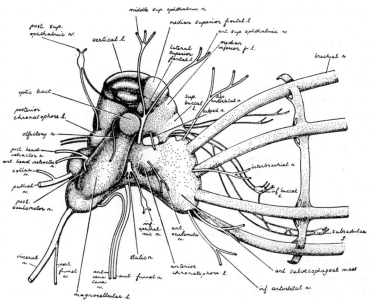

Fig. 13. Octopus brain is viewed laterally with the right optic lobe removed. The main external anatomical features of the brain and nerve connexions are labelled. As is the case with many invertebrate brains, the brain of *Octopus vulgaris* completely surrounds the animal's œsophagus. (Diagram provided by courtesy of J. Z. Young.)

octopus learns to discriminate by touch and by sight just as readily as a mammal. Yet the general structure and organization of the cephalopod brain bears no resemblance to the mammalian brain. This brain (Fig. 13) consists of a number of lobes around the gullet. From their work and that of Wells (1959), it seems that visual and tactile memory systems can be assigned to the vertical and sub-frontal lobes, respectively. Furthermore these lobes seem to function on a mass action basis.

The lack of success in finding cross-species differences for learning is perhaps due to the elementary nature of the tasks used. It is unlikely that differences in intelligence between species would emerge in terms of the speed of data processing. It would be more reasonable to expect differences in adjustment to more complex data processing problems; and Bitterman (1965) has reported some interesting species differences for learning-set and probability-learning tasks.

A learning-set task requires the animal first to learn a two-choice discrimination for either a spatial or a visual task. On reaching the required standard of success to one stimulus, the animal has to relearn the task to the other stimulus. On attainment of successful responding to this stimulus, the animal has to revert once again to the other stimulus and so forth. Monkeys or rats trained in this way show a steady and progressive improvement with successive reversals. Gradually each reversal is obtained more quickly and with fewer errors as the animal "learns to learn" (Harlow, 1949). A fish, in contrast, shows no improvement at all for either spatial or visual discrimination. Late reversals are gained no more readily than the early ones. On the other hand, the turtle showed no learning-set for visual problems, but did acquire a learning-set for spatial problems (Bitterman, 1965).

Species differences have also been found for probability-learning tasks. In such tasks, alternative A would be rewarded, over a random sequence of trials, 70% of the time; and alternative B would be rewarded for the remaining 30% of the time. The monkey or rat exposed to such a problem typically "maximizes", that is it selects the more probable stimulus in almost all trials. Occasionally, a different strategy of reacting is found where the animal "matches" choice and reward; in other words, its choice-ratio approximates the reward-ratio. This "matching" of choices to reward probabilities can follow differing patterns in the monkey and in the rat. Bitterman (1965) has indicated that in the rat there is a tendency to "match" due to reward-following (a tendency on each trial to choose the alternative that was rewarded on the previous trial). When "matching" occurs in the monkey it is due to the opposite strategy of avoiding the previously rewarded alternative (Wilson, Oscar and Bitterman, 1964). In the fish "matching" appears as a random adjustment for both visual and spatial tasks, no sequential pattern being discernible in the choice made (Behrend and Bitterman, 1951). Experiments by Kirk and Bitterman (1965) on probability learning in the turtle give results similar to those for learning-set problems. Random "matching" was found for visual problems whereas for spatial problems the animal either "maximized" or "matched" by reward-following.

This approach of studying the "strategies" adopted in complex learning tasks by different species is a most interesting recent development. The initial results found by Bitterman and his co-workers seem to point to definite differences between species in the "strategies" used by differing brains in the adjustment to situations requiring either the formation-learning of learning-sets, or an analysis of the probability of reward.

The effect of decortication in the rat was to abolish probability "maximizing" and leave the animal with a type of probability "matching" analogous to that in animals with more primitive brains (Gonzalez, Roberts and Bitterman, 1964). The inference from these experiments is that the evolution of the cortex enables the brain to deal with ambiguous learning situations by more flexible methods of probability analysis is a new and stimulating approach. It would certainly seem to be an important new development in the study of the significance of cortical factors in learning.

Summary and conclusions Recent experimentation on neural mechanisms of memory has been reviewed and an attempt has been made to place the experimental findings within an acceptable conceptual framework. It is felt that commitment in the past to an interpretation of learning or memory as a single unitary concept has not been helpful in the search for brain mechanisms.

Considering memory as a form of information processing by the brain has revealed quite clearly that memory is the outcome of several differing forms of sensory analysis. Memory involves far more than a simple storage of information. The evidence reviewed indicates that different types of learning probably have different storage sites in the brain. It seems that associative learning involves essentially subcortical mechanisms, whereas contingency learning is cortically stored.

It has been conjectured that "short-term" memory refers to the labile nature of memory just after learning. It appears that some form of continuing, or perseverative, change is involved in the consolidation of a permanent memory trace. Interference with this consolidation process is found to impair memory storage. However, there is little evidence to support the notion that either the temporal or the prefrontal cortex are sites for the consolidation of memory: the removal of the prefrontal cortex produces impairment of attention rather than immediate memory defects. In fact, short-term and long-term memory refer to different stages in the process of consolidation.

The recent findings in comparative studies of the cerebral cortex seem to hold promise for future development. It is tempting to speculate on the possible importance of this work. However, without further confirmation it might be premature. Certainly the notion that encephalization leads to different types of learning is one which should prove fruitful.

References

Abt, J. P., Essman, W. B. and Jarvik, M. E. (1961), *Science*, **133**, 1477.
Adey, W. R., Dunlop, C. W. and Hendrix, C. E. (1960), *Arch. Neurol.*, **3**, 74.
Adey, W. R., Segundo, J. P. and Livingston, R. B. (1957), *J. Neurophysiol.*, **20**, 1.
Anrep, G. V. (1923), *Proc. roy. Soc. B*, **94**, 404.

Arden, G. B. and Söderberg, U. (1959), *Experientia*, **15**, 163.
Arden, G. B. and Söderberg, U. (1961), In *Sensory Communication* (Edited by W. A. Rosenblith), M.I.T. Press & Wiley, New York.
Ashby, W. R. (1952), *Design for a Brain*, Wiley, New York.
Asratyan, E. A. (1961), In *CIOMS Symposium on Brain Mechanisms and Learning* (Edited by J. F. Delafresnaye, A. Fessard and J. Konorski), Blackwell Scientific Publications, Oxford.
Bass, M. J. and Hull, C. L. (1934), *J. comp. Psychol.*, **46**, 241.
Beck, E. C., Doty, R. W. and Kooi, K. A. (1958), *Electroenceph. clin. Neurophysiol.*, **10**, 279.
Behrend, E. R. and Bitterman, M. E. (1951), *Amer. J. Psychol.*, **74**, 542.
Bernstein, A. L. (1934), *J. gen. Psychol.*, **10**, 173.
Bitterman, M. E. (1960), *Amer. J. Psychol.*, **15**, 704.
Bitterman, M. E. (1965), *Sci. Amer.*, **212**, Jan., 92.
Bloch, V. and Hebb, D. (1956), *Psychologie Française*, **1**, 8.
Blodgett, H. C. (1929), *Univ. Calif. Publ. Psychol.*, **4**, 113.
Boneau, C. A. (1958), *J. exp. Psychol.*, **56**, 464.
Boycott, B. and Young, J. Z. (1950), *Symp. Soc. exp. Biol.*, **4**, 432.
Bradley, P. B. and Mollica, A. (1958), *Arch. ital. Biol.*, **96**, 168.
Brady, J. V. (1951), *J. comp. physiol. Psychol.*, **44**, 507.
Braun, H. W., Russell, R. W. and Patton, R. A. (1949a), *J. comp. physiol. Psychol.*, **42**, 87.
Braun, H. W., Russell, R. W. and Patton, R. A. (1949b), *J. comp. physiol. Psychol.*, **42**, 322.
Breen, R. A. and McGaugh, J. L. (1961), *J. comp. physiol. Psychol.*, **54**, 498.
Bromiley, R. B. (1948), *J. comp. physiol. Psychol.*, **41**, 102.
Brown, S. and Schäfer, E. A. (1888), *Phil. Trans. Roy. Soc. Lond. B*, 179, 303.
Brust-Carmona, H., Bach-y-Rita, G., Penaloza-Rojas, J. and Hernandez-Peon, R. (1960), *Resum. III Congr. mex. Cienc. fisiol.*, 35.
Bureš, J. and Burešovà, O. (1960), *J. comp. physiol. Psychol.*, **53**, 358.
Bureš, J. and Burešovà, O. (1964), *J. comp. physiol. Psychol.*, **57**, 326.
Burns, B. D. (1958), *The Mammalian and Cerebral Cortex*, Arnold, London.
Buser, D. and Rougeul, A. (1956), *Rev. neurol.*, **95**, 501.
Butler, R., Diamond, I. and Neff, W. (1957), *J. Neurophysiol.*, **20**, 108.
Calvin, J. S. (1939), Ph.D. dissertation, Yale University.
Cason, H. (1935), *J. exp. Psychol.*, **18**, 599.
Chevalier, J. A. (1965), *J. comp. physiol. Psychol.*, **59**, 125.
Chow, K. L. (1951), *Comp. Psychol. Monogr.*, **20**, 187.
Chow, K. L. (1952), *J. comp. physiol. Psychol.*, **45**, 109.
Chow, K. L. (1954), *J. comp. physiol. Psycho.*, **47**, 194.
Chow, K. L. (1961), In *CIOMS Symposium on Brain Mechanisms and Learning* (Edited by J. F. Delafresnaye, A. Fessard and J. Konorski), Blackwell Scientific Publications, Oxford.
Chow, K. L. and Orbach, J. (1957), *J. comp. physiol. Psychol.*, **50**, 636.
Chow, K. L. and Survis, J. (1958), *Arch. Neurol. Psychiat. Chic.*, **79**, 640.
Cohen, J. (1950), *J. comp. physiol. Psychol.*, **43**, 211.
Coons, E. E. and Miller, M. E. (1960), *J. comp. physiol. Psychol.*, **53**, 524.
Cordeau, J. P. and Mahut, H. (1964), *Brain*, **87**, 177.
Culler, E. A. and Mettler, F. A. (1934), *J. comp. Psychol.*, **18**, 291.
Debold, R. C., Jensen, D. and Miller, N. E. (1965), *J. comp. physiol. Psychol.*, **59**, 102
Dennis, W. (1929), *J. genet. Psychol.*, **36**, 59.
Dorcus, R. M. and Gray, W. L. (1932), *J. comp. physiol. Psychol.*, **13**, 447.
Dostalek, C. and Figar, S. (1956), *Physiol. bohemoslov.*, **5**, Suppl. 7.
Doty, R. W. (1958), In *CNS and Behavior*, p. 241 (Edited by M. A. B. Brazier), Josiah Macy, Jr. Foundation, New York.
Doty, R. W., Beck, E. C. and Kooi, K. A. (1959), *Exp. Neurol.*, **1**, 360–85.
Doty, R. W. and Giurgea, C. (1961), In *CIOMS Symposium on Brain Mechanisms and Learning* (Edited by J. F. Delafresnaye, A. Fessard and J. Konorski), Blackwell Scientific Publications, Oxford.
Doty, R. W., Rutledge, L. T. and Larsen, R. M. (1956), *J. Neurophysiol.*, **19**, 401.
Downer, J. L. de C. (1958), *Fed. Proc.*, **17**, 37.
Downer, J. L. de C. (1959), *Brain*, **82**, 251.

Downer, J. L. de C. (1962), In *Interhemispheric Relations and Cerebral Dominance* (Edited by V. B. Mountcastle), Johns Hopkins Press, Baltimore.
Downer, J. L. de C. (1963), *Endeavour*, 22, No. 87, 138.
Duncan, C. P. (1949), *J. comp. physiol. Psychol.*, 42, 32.
Egger, M. D. and Miller, N. E. (1962), *J. exp. Psychol.*, 64, 97.
Egger, M. D. and Miller, N. E. (1963), *J. comp. physiol. Psychol.*, 56, 132.
Ellingson, R. J. (1958), *Electroenceph. clin. Neurophysiol.*, 10, 31.
Ericksen, S. E. (1939a), *J. comp. Psychol.*, 27, 373.
Ericksen, S. E. (1939b), *J. comp. Psychol.*, 28, 45.
Essman, W. B. and Jarvik, M. E. (1961), *Psychopharmacologia*, 2, 172.
Estes, W. K. (1960), *Psychol. Rev.*, 67, 207.
Evans, S. (1936), *J. genet. Psychol.*, 48, 177–98.
Fernandez-Guardiola, A., Roldin, E., Fanjul, M. L. and Castells, C. (1961), *Electroenceph. clin. Neurophysiol.*, 12, 575.
Ferster, C. B. and Skinner, B. F. (1957), *Schedules of Reinforcement*, Appleton-Century-Crofts, New York.
Finan, J. L. (1939), *J. Neurophysiol.*, 2, 208.
Finan, J. L. (1942), *Amer. J. Psychol.*, 55, 202.
Finley, C. B. (1941), *J. comp. Neurol.*, 74, 203.
Fitzwater, M. E. and Riesman, M. N. (1952), *J. exp. Psychol.*, 44, 211.
Fitzwater, M. E. and Thrush, R. S. (1956), *J. exp. Psychol.*, 51, 59.
French, J. D., von Amerongen M. and Magoun, H. W. (1952), *Arch. Neurol. Psychiat., Chic.*, 68, 577.
Fuster, J. M. (1957), *Fed. Proc.*, 16, 43.
Galambos, R. (1958), In *The Central Nervous System and Behaviour* (Edited by M. Brazier), Josiah Macy, Jr. Foundation, New York.
Galambos, R., Sheatz, G. and Vernier, V. G. (1956), *Science*, 123, 376.
Gardner, L. P. and Nissen, H. W. (1948), *J. genet. Psychol.*, 72, 145.
Gastaut, H. (1958), In *Neurological Basis of Behaviour (Ciba Symp.)*, p. 255 (Edited by G. E. W. Wolstenholme and C. M. O'Connor), Churchill, London.
Gershuni, G. V., Kozhevnikov, V. A., Maruseva, A. M., Avakyan, R. V., Radionova, E. A., Altman, J. A. and Soroko, V. I. (1960), In *Moscow Colloquium on Electroencephalography of Higher Nervous Activity* (Edited by H. H. Jasper and G. D. Smirnov), *Electroenceph. clin. Neurophysiol.*, Suppl. 13, 115.
Girden, E., Mettler, F. A., Finch, C. and Culler, E. (1936), *J. comp. Psychol.*, 21, 367.
Glees, P. and Cole, J. (1950), *J. Neurophysiol.*, 13, 137.
Glickman, S. E. (1958), *Canad. J. Psychol.*, 12, 97.
Gonzalez, R. C., Roberts, W. A. and Bitterman, M. E. (1964), *Amer. J. Psychol.*, 77, 547.
Grastyan, E. (1959), In *Central Nervous System and Behavior* (Edited by M. A. B. Brazier), Josiah Macy, Jr. Foundation, New York.
Grastyan, E. and Karmos, G. (1961), In *Physiologie de l'Hippocampe*, Colloque Intern. du CNRS (Edited by J. Cadilhac), Montpellier, Paris.
Grastyan, E., Lissak, K. and Kekesi, F. (1956), *Acta physiol. hung.*, 9, 138.
Green, J. D. (1964), *Physiol. Rev.*, 44, 561.
Grice, G. R. (1948), *J. exp. Psychol.*, 30, 475.
Griffith, C. R. (1924), *J. comp. Psychol.*, 4, 137.
Hagbarth, K. E. and Höjeberg, J. (1957), *Nature, Lond.*, 179, 526.
Hagbarth, K. E. and Kerr, D. I. B. (1954), *J. Neurophysiol.*, 18, 388.
Hansche, W. J. and Grant, D. A. (1960), *J. exp. Psychol.*, 59, 19.
Harlow, H. F. (1949), *Psychol. Rev.*, 56, 51.
Hearst, E., Beer, B., Sheatz, G. and Galambos, R. (1960), *Electroenceph. clin. Neurophysiol.*, 12, 137.
Hebb, D. O. (1949), *The Organization of Behavior*, Wiley, New York.
Hebb, D. O. and Penfield, W. (1940), *Arch. Neurol. Psych., Lond.*, 44, 421.
Heriot, J. T. and Coleman, P. D. (1962), *J. comp. physiol. Psychol.*, 55, 1082.
Hernandez-Peon, R. (1960), In *Moscow Colloquium on Electroencephalography of Higher Nervous Activity* (Edited by H. H. Jasper and G. D. Smirnov), *Electroenceph. clin. Neurophysiol.*, Suppl. 13.
Hernandez-Peon, R. (1961), In *Sensory Communication* (Edited by W. A. Rosenblith), M.I.T. Press & Wiley, New York.

M

Hernandez-Peon, R. and Brust-Carmona, H. (1961), In *CIOMS Symposium on Brain Mechanisms and Learning* (Edited by J. F. Delafresnaye, A. Fessard and J. Konorski), Blackwell Scientific Publications, Oxford.
Hernandez-Peon, R., Guzman-Flores, C., Alcaraz, M. and Fernandez-Guardiola, (1957), *Acta neurol. latinoamer.*, **3**, 1–8.
Hernandez-Peon, R. and Scherrer, H. (1955), *Fed. Proc.*, **14**, 71.
Hernandez-Peon, R., Scherrer, H. and Jouvet, M. (1956), *Science*, p. 23, 331.
Hernandez-Peon, R., Scherrer, H. and Velasco, M. (1956), *Acta neurol. latinoamer.*, **2**, 8.
Hilgard, E. R. and Humphreys, L. C. (1938), *J. gen. Psychol.*, **19**, 111.
Hilgard, E. R. and Marquis, D. G. (1935). *J. comp. Psychol.*, **19**, 29.
Hilgard, E. R. and Marquis, D. G. (1940), *Conditioning and Learning*, Appleton-Century-Crofts, New York.
Holmes, J. E. and Adey, W. R. (1960), *Amer. J. Physiol.*, **199**, 741.
Honzik, C. H. (1936), *J. comp. Psychol.*, *Mongr.*, **13**, No. 64.
Horn, G. (1960), *Brain*, **83**, 57.
Hovland, C. I. (1936), *Proc. nat. Acad. Sci.*, *Wash.*, **22**, 430.
Hovland, C. I. (1937), *J. gen. Psychol.*, **17**, 125.
Hu, C. N. (1938), *J. gen. Psychol.*, **18**, 267.
Hugelin, A., Dumont, S. and Paillas, N. (1960), *Science*, **131**, 1371.
Hughlings Jackson, J. (1888), *Brain*, **11**, 179.
Hull, C. L. (1943), *Principles of Behavior*, Appleton-Century-Crofts, New York.
Hunter, W. S. (1930a), *J. genet. Psychol.*, **38**, 3.
Hunter, W. S. (1930b), *J. gen. Psychol.*, **3**, 455.
Hunter, W. S. (1931), *J. gen. Psychol.*, **5**, 230.
Isaacson, R. L., Douglas, R. J. and Moore, R. Y. (1961), *J. comp. physiol. Psychol.*, **54**, 625.
Jacobsen, C. F. (1932), *Proc. Ass. Res. nerv. Dis.*, **13**, 225.
Jacobsen, C. F. (1935), *Arch. Neurol. Psychiat.*, *Chic.*, **33**, 558.
Jarvik, M. E. (1964), In *Animal Behaviour and Drug Action* (*Ciba Symp.*) (Edited by H. Steinberg), Churchill, London.
John, E. R. and Killam, K. F. (1959), *J. Pharmacol. exp. Ther.*, **125**, 252.
Jouvet, M. and Hernandez-Peon, R. (1957), *Electroenceph. clin. Neurophysiol.*, Suppl. 6, 39.
Kaada, B. R., Rasmussen, E. W. and Kveim, O. (1961), *Exp. Neurol.*, **3**, 333.
Kappauf, W. E. and Schlosberg, H. (1937), *J. gen. Psychol.*, **50**, 27.
Kellog, W. N. and Wolf, I. S. (1939), *J. exp. Psychol.*, **24**, 366.
Killam, K. F. and Killam, E. K. (1958), *Henry Ford Hosp. int. Symp.* (Edited by H. H. Jasper *et al.*), *RF of the Brain*, Little Brown, Boston.
Killam, K. F. and Killam, E. K. (1959), *Res. Publ. Ass. nerv. ment. Dis.*, **37**, 245.
Kimble, G. A. (1947), *J. exp. Psychol.*, **37**, 1.
Kimble, G. A., Mann, L. J. and Dufort, R. H. (1955), *J. exp. Psychol.*, **49**, 407.
King, F. A. (1958), *J. nerv. ment. Dis.*, **126**, 57.
King, R. A. (1965), *J. comp. physiol. Psychol.*, **59**, 283.
Kirk, K. L. and Bitterman, M. E. (1965), *Science*, **148**, 1484.
Kluver, H. and Bucy, P. C. (1938), *J. Psychol.*, **5**, 33.
Köhler, W. (1925), *The Mentality of Apes*, Harcourt-Brace, New York.
Konorski, J. (1948), *Conditioned Reflexes and Nervous Organization*, University Press, Cambridge.
Konorski, J. (1961), In *CIOMS Symposium on Brain Mechanisms and Learning* (Edited by J. F. Delafresnaye, A. Fessard and J. Konorski), Blackwell Scientific Publications, Oxford.
Kretchevsky, I. (1933), *J. comp. Psychol.*, **16**, 99.
Larrson, L. E., Nelin, K. A., Nordstrohm-Ohrberg, G., Silfverskiold, B. P. and Ohrberg, K. (1954), *Acta psychol. neurol. scand.*, **95**, 1.
Lashley, K. S. (1917a), *Amer. J. Physiol.*, **43**, 169.
Lashley, K. S. (1917b), *Psychobiology*, **1**, 141.
Lashley, K. S. (1918), *Psychobiology*, **1**, 353.
Lashley, K. S. (1924), *Arch. Neurol. Psychiat.*, *Chic.*, **12**, 249.
Lashley, K. S. (1929a), In *The Foundations of Experimental Psychology* (Edited by C. Murchison), Clark University Press, Worcester, Mass.
Lashley, K. S. (1929b), *Brain Mechanisms and Intelligence*, University Press, Chicago.

Lashley, K. S. (1935), *Psychol. Monogr.*, **11**, 43.
Lashley, K. S. (1939), *J. comp. Neurol.*, **70**, 45.
Lashley, K. S. (1942), *J. genet. Psychol.*, **60**, 197.
Lashley, K. S. (1943), *J. comp. Neurol.*, **79**, 431.
Lashley, K. S. (1950), *Symp. Soc. exp. Biol.*, **4**, 454.
Lashley, K. S. and McCarthy, D. H. (1926), *J. comp. Psychol.*, **6**, 423.
Lebedinskaia, S. I. and Rosenthal, J. S. (1935), *Brain*, **58**, 412.
Leboucq, G. (1929), *Mem. Acad. R. Belg.*, **10**, 55.
Leukel, F. P. (1957), *J. comp. physiol. Psychol.*, **50**, 300.
Liddell, H. S., James, W. T. and Anderson, O. D. (1934), *Comp. Psychol. Monogr.*, **11**, No. 51.
Light, J. S. and Gantt, W. H. (1936), *J. comp. Psychol.*, **21**, 19.
Lindsley, D. B. (1958), In *Reticular Formation of the Brain* (Edited by H. H. Jasper *et al.*), Little Brown, Boston.
Loucks, R. B. (1933), *J. comp. Psychol.*, **16**, 439.
Macfarlane, D. A. (1930), *Univ. Calif. Publ. Psychol.*, **4**, 277.
Maclean, P., Flanigan, S., Flynn, J., Kim, C. and Stevens, J. (1955), *Yale J. Biol. Med.*, **28**, 380.
McAllister, W. R. (1953a), *J. exp. Psychol.*, **45**, 417.
McAllister, W. R. (1953b), *J. exp. Psychol.*, **45**, 423.
McCleary, R. A. (1960), *J. comp. physiol. Psychol.*, **53**, 311.
McGaugh, J. L., Thompson, C. W., Westbrook, W. H. and Hadspeth, W. J. (1962), *Psychopharmacologia*, **3**, 352.
McGaugh, J. L. and Petinovich, L. (1959), *Amer. J. Psychol.*, **72**, 1, 99.
McGaugh, J. L., Westbrook, W., and Burt, C. (1961), *J. comp. physiol. Psychol.*, **54**, 502.
McGaugh, J. L., Westbrook, W. H. and Thompson, C. W. (1962), *J. comp. physiol. Psychol.*, **55**, 710.
Madsen, M. C. and McGaugh, J. C. (1961), *J. comp. physiol. Psychol.*, **54**, 522.
Malmo, R. B. (1942), *J. Neurophysiol.*, **5**, 295.
Marquis, D. G. (1935). *Arch. Neurol. Psychiat.*, **33**, 807.
Marquis, D. G. and Hilgard, E. R. (1936), *J. comp. Psychol.*, **22**, 157.
Meehl, P. E. and MacCorquodale, K. (1948), *J. comp. physiol. Psychol.*, **41**, 372.
Meickle, T. H., Sechzer, J. A. and Stellar, E. (1962), *J. Neurophysiol.*, **25**, 530.
Meyer, J. S. and Denny-Brown, D. (1955), *Electroenceph. clin. Neurophysiol.*, **7**, 529.
Miller, N. E. (1961), *Presidential Address to American Psychological Assoc.*, New York.
Milner, B. and Penfield, W. (1955), *Trans. Amer. neurol. Ass.*, **80**, 42.
Mirsky, A. F. and Rosvold, H. E. (1953), *J. comp. physiol. Psychol.*, **46**, 153.
Mishkin, M. (1954), *J. comp. physiol. Psychol.*, **47**, 187.
Mishkin, M. and Hall, M. (1955), *J. comp. physiol. Psychol.*, **48**, 97.
Mishkin, M. and Pribram, K. H. (1954), *J. comp. physiol. Psychol.*, **47**, 14.
Mishkin, M., Rosvold, H. E. and Pribram, K. H. (1953), *J. Neurophysiol.*, **16**, 155.
Moeller, G. (1954), *J. exp. Psychol.*, **48**, 162.
Morrell, I., Naquet, R. and Gastaut, H. (1957), *J. Neurophysiol.*, **20**, 574.
Moushegian, G., Rupert, A., Marsh, J. T. and Galambos, R. (1961), *Science*, **133**, 582.
Mowrer, O. H. and Jones, H. M. (1943), *J. exp. Psychol.*, **33**, 369.
Mowrer, O. H. and Jones, H. M. (1945), *J. exp. Psychol.*, **35**, 293.
Muenzinger, K. F. and Conrad, D. G. (1953), *J. comp. physiol. Psychol.*, **46**, 1.
Muller, G. E. and Pilzecker, A. (1900), *Z. Psychol. Physiol. Sinnesorg*, **1**, 1.
Munn, N. L. (1950), *Handbook of Psychological Research on the Rat*, Houghton-Mifflin, Boston.
Myers, R. E. (1955), *J. comp. physiol. Psychol.*, **48**, 470.
Myers, R. E. (1956), *Brain*, **79**, 358.
Myers, R. E. (1962), In *Interhemispheric Relations and Cerebral Dominance* (Edited by V. B. Mountcastle), Johns Hopkins Press, Baltimore.
Nagaty, M. O. (1951a), *J. exp. Psychol.*, **42**, 239.
Nagaty, M. O. (1951b), *J. exp. Psychol.*, **42**, 333.
Naquet, R., Regis, H., Fischer-Williams, M. and Fernandez-Guardiola, A. (1960), *Brain*, **83**, 52.

Nauta, W. J. H. and Kuypers, H. G. J. M. (1958), In *Reticular Formation of the Brain* (Edited by H. H. Jasper *et al.*), Little-Brown, Boston.
Newman, H. H. (1926), *The Nature of the World and of Man*, University of Chicago Press, Chicago.
Ochs, S. (1962), *Int. Rev. Neurobiol.*, **4**, 1.
Orbach, J. (1959), *AMA Arch. Neurol. Psychiat.*, **81**, 49.
Orbach, J. and Fantz, R. L. (1958), *J. exp. physiol. Psychol.*, **51**, 126.
Orbach, J., Milner, B. and Rasmussen, T. (1960), *Arch. Neurol.*, **3**, 230.
Palestini, M., Rossi, G. F. and Zanchetti, A. (1957), *Arch. ital. Biol.*, **95**, 97.
Pare, W. (1961), *J. comp. physiol. Psychol.*, **54**, 506.
Pavlov, I. P. (1928), *Conditioned Reflexes. An Investigation of the Physiological Activity of the Cerebral Cortex*, University Press, Oxford.
Pearlman, C. A., Sharpless, S. K. and Jarvik, M. E. (1961), *J. comp. physiol. Psychol.*, **54**, 109.
Perin, C. T. (1943), *J. exp. Psychol.*, **32**, 37.
Perkins, C. C. (1947), *J. exp. Psychol.*, **46**, 225.
Poltyrev, S. S. (1936), *Z. Biol.*, **97**, 180.
Poltyrev, S. S. and Zeliony, G. P. (1930), *Z. Biol.*, **90**, 157.
Porter, J. M. (1938), *J. exp. Psychol.*, **23**, 403.
Pribram, K. H. (1950), *J. Neurophysiol.*, **13**, 373.
Pribram, K. H. and Barry, J. (1956), *J. Neurophysiol.*, **19**, 99.
Ransmeier, R. E. and Gerard, R. W. (1954), *Amer. J. Physiol.*, **179**, 663.
Razran, G. H. S. (1933), *Psychol. Bull.*, **30**, 261.
Razran, G. H. S. (1956), *Psychol. Rev.*, **63**, 39.
Rey, A. (1938), *Arch. Psychol., Genève*, **27**, 1.
Rey, A. (1939), *J. Psychol. norm. path.*, **36**, 424.
Reynolds, B. (1945), *J. exp. Psychol.*, **35**, 81.
Reynolds, W. F. (1958), *J. exp. Psychol.*, **55**, 335.
Roitbak, A. K. (1960), In *Moscow Colloquium on Electroencephalography of Higher Nervous Activity* (Edited by H. H. Jasper and G. D. Smirnov), *Electroenceph. clin. Neurophysiol.*, Suppl. 13.
Ross, L. E. (1959), *J. exp. Psychol.*, **57**, 74.
Ross, R. B. (1964), *Nature, Lond.*, **201**, 109.
Ross, R. B. and Russell, I. S. (1964), *Nature, Lond.*, **204**, No. 4961, 909.
Ross, R. B. and Russell, I. S. (1965), In press.
Ross, R. B. and Russell, I. S. (1966), In press.
Russell, I. S. and Ochs, S. (1960), *Physiologist*, **3**, 3.
Russell, I. S. and Ochs, S. (1963), *Brain*, **86**, 37.
Russell, I. S., Kleinman, D. and Plotkin, H. R. (In preparation).
Russell, I. S., Ross, R. B. and Strongman, K. (1964), *Amer. Psychologist*, **19**, 509.
Russell, W. R. and Nathan, P. W. (1946), *Brain*, **69**, 280.
Sager, O., Wendt, G., Moisanu, M. and Cirnu, V. (1956), Cited in *Neurological Basis of Behaviour* (Edited by G. E. W. Wolstenholme and C. M. O'Connor), Little Brown, Boston.
Schneiderman, N. and Gormezano, I. (1964), *J. comp. physiol. Psychol.*, **57**, 188.
Scoville, W. B. and Milner, B. (1957), *Neurol. Neurosurg. Psychiat.*, **20**, 11.
Segundo, J. P., Roig, J. A. and Sommer-Smith, J. A. (1959), *Electroenceph. clin. Neurophysiol.*, **11**, 471.
Sharpless, S. and Jasper, H. H. (1956), *Brain*, **79**, 655.
Skinner, B. F. (1937), *J. gen. Psychol.*, **12**, 66.
Skinner, B. F. (1938), *The Behavior of Organisms*, Appleton-Century-Crofts, New York.
Sokolov, E. N. (1960), In *CNS and Behavior, III*, p. 187 (Edited by M. A. B. Brazier), Josiah Macy, Jr. Foundation, New York.
Solomon, R. L. (1948), *Psychol. Bull.*, **45**, 1.
Soloveychik, D. I. (1940), Cited in *Conditioned Reflexes and Nervous Organization* (Edited by J. Konorski), University Press, Cambridge.
Spence, K. W. (1956), *Behavior Theory and Conditioning*, Yale University Press, New Haven.
Spence, K. W. and Norris, E. B. (1950), *J. exp. Psychol.*, **40**, 716.
Sperry, R. W. (1956), In *Biological and Biochemical Bases of Behavior* (Edited by H. F. Harlow and C. W. Woolsey), University of Wisconsin, Madison.

Sperry, R. W. (1961), *Science*, **133**, 1749.
Sperry, R. W. (1964), *Sci. Amer.*, **210**, Jan., 42.
Sperry, R. W., Stamm, J. S. and Miner, N. (1956), *J. comp. physiol. Psychol.*, **49**, 529.
Spooner, A. and Kellog, W. N. (1947), *Amer. J. Psychol.*, **60**, 321.
Stamm, J. S. and Sperry, R. W. (1957), *J. comp. physiol. Psychol.*, **50**, 138.
Stepien, L. S., Cordeau, J. P. and Rasmussen, T. (1960), *Brain*, **83**, 470.
Stern, J. A. (1956a), *Psychol. Rep.*, **2**, 314.
Stern, J. A. (1956b), *J. comp. physiol. Psychol.*, **49**, 411.
Suzuki, H. and Taira, N. (1961), *Jap. J. Physiol.*, **11**, 641.
Talland, G. A. (1960), *J. nerv. ment. Dis.*, **130**, 366.
Ten Cate, J. (1934), *Arch. neerd. Physiol.*, **19**, 469.
Teuber, H. L. (1955), *Ann. Rev. Psychol.*, **6**, 267.
Thompson, C. W., McGaugh, J. C., Smith, C. E., Hudspeth, W. J. and Westbrook, W. H. (1961), *Canad. J. Psychol.*, **15**, 67.
Thompson, R. (1957), *J. comp. physiol. Psychol.*, **50**, 397.
Thompson, R. (1958), *J. comp. physiol. Psychol.*, **51**, 644.
Thompson, R. and Dean, W. (1955), *J. comp. physiol. Psychol.*, **48**, 488.
Thorpe, W. H. (1950), In *Symp. Soc. exp. Biol.*, **4**, 387.
Tolman, E. C. (1932), *Purposive Behavior in Animals and Men*, Appleton-Century-Crofts, New York.
Tolman, E. C. and Honzik, C. H. (1930), *Univ. Calif. Publ. Psychol.*, **4**, 257.
Tonini, G. (1964), Personal communication.
Travis, R. P. (1964), *J. comp. physiol. Psychol.*, **57**, 42.
Trevarthen, C. B. (1960), *Amer. Psychologist*, **15**, 485.
Trotter, W. (1924), *Lancet*, **1**, 935.
Tsang, Y. S. (1934), *Comp. Psychol. Monogr.*, **10**, 1.
Tsang, Y. S. (1936), *Comp. Psychol. Monogr.*, **12**, No. 57.
Vandermeer, S. and Amsel, A. (1952), *J. exp. Psychol.*, **43**, 261.
Wade, M. (1947), *J. Neurophysiol.*, **10**, 57.
Warren, J. M. and Akert, K. (1964), (Eds), *The Frontal Granular Cortex and Behavior*, McGraw-Hill, New York.
Watson, J. (1917), *Psychobiology*, **1**, 51.
Weisman, A. (1963), *J. comp. physiol. Psychol.*, **56**, 806.
Wells, M. J. (1959), *J. exp. Biol.*, **36**, 590.
Wendt, G. R. (1936), *Psychol. Rev.*, **43**, 258.
White, C. T. and Schlosberg, H. (1952), *J. exp. Psychol.*, **43**, 357.
Wilson, M. (1957), *J. comp. physiol. Psychol.*, **50**, 630.
Wilson, W. A. and Mishkin, M. (1959), *J. comp. physiol. Psychol.*, **52**, 10.
Wilson, W. A., Oscar, M. and Bitterman, M. E. (1964), *Quart. J. exp. Psychol.*, **16**, 163.
Wing, K. G. (1946), *Amer. J. Psychol.*, **59**, 583.
Wing, K. G. (1947), *Amer. J. Psychol.*, **60**, 30.
Wing, K. G. and Smith, K. U. (1942), *J. exp. Psychol.*, **31**, 478.
Wolfe, J. B. (1934), *J. comp. Psychol.*, **17**, 1.
Wolfle, H. M. (1930), *J. gen. Psychol.*, **4**, 372.
Wolfle, H. M. (1932), *J. gen. Psychol.*, **7**, 80.
Young, J. Z. (1964), *A Model of the Brain*, University Press, Oxford.
Yoshii, N. (1957), *Electroenceph. clin. Neurophysiol.*, Suppl. 6, 75.
Yoshii, N. and Hockaday, W. T. (1958), *Electroenceph. clin. Neurophysiol.*, **10**, 487.
Yoshii, N., Matsumoto, J., Ogura, H., Shimokochi, M., Yamaguchi, Y. and Yamasaki, H. (1960), In *Moscow Colloquium on Electroencephalography of Higher Nervous Activity* (Edited by H. H. Jasper and G. S. Smirnov), *Electroenceph. clin. Neurophysiol.*, Suppl. 13.
Yoshii, N., Pruvot, P. and Gastaut, H. (1957), *Electroenceph. clin. Neurophysiol.* **9**, 595.
Zeliony, G. P. (1929), *Rev. Médecine*, **46**, 181.
Zeliony, G. P. and Kadykov, B. I. (1938), *Psychol. Abstr.*, **12**, No. 5829.
Zener, K. (1937), *Amer. J. Psychol.*, **50**, 384.

Author Index

Index